Deprivation of Liberty Safeguards (DoLS)
Handbook

First Edition

Written by

*Steven Richards BA (Hons)* and *Aasya F Mughal LLB (Hons) Barrister*

www.Bookswise.org.uk

First edition

Published November 2015
BooksWise Publications Ltd

British Library Cataloguing in Publication Data
A catalogue record for this book is available from the British Library

ISBN 978-0-9931324-0-7



Printed and bound by the CPI Group (UK) Ltd, Croydon CR0 4YY

*'... it seems to me, what it means to be deprived of liberty must be the same for everyone, whether or not they have physical or mental disabilities. If it would be a deprivation of my liberty to be obliged to live in a particular place, subject to constant monitoring and control, only allowed out with close supervision, and unable to move away without permission even if such an opportunity became available, then it must also be a deprivation of the liberty of a disabled person.'*

Lady Justice Hale, Supreme Court
Case: *P v Cheshire West & Chester Council, P & Q v Surrey CC [2014] UKSC 19*

*'Although some may baulk at the idea of 100,000 DOLS applications a year, we should remember that every one of those applications represents a person having their care independently scrutinised. DOLS can help to shine a light on care that is unnecessarily restrictive and does not put the person's views first and foremost. Therefore, we should strongly back the principles of DOLS.'*

Alistair Burt, Minister of State for Community and Social Care
House of Commons debate, 17 June 2015 [1]

*He that would make his own liberty secure, must guard even his enemy from oppression; for if he violates this duty, he establishes a precedent that will reach to himself.*

Thomas Paine (1737-1809)

*Thank you from the authors*

Steven Richards

My family for all their support.

Aasya F Mughal

My parents Salahuddin and Azra Mughal for their selfless encouragement and support and my closest friends Labeeba, Tracy, Debbie and Raminder, for *always* listening and being supportive even though they now all know more about *Cheshire West* than they ever really wanted to.

Special thanks from both authors:

To all the delegates in courses and conferences we have met over the years. Especially those that have questioned, challenged and debated with us. A lot of what we hope is useful information in this book would not have come to us if it were not for this interaction with all of you. Thank you.

# Contents

# Introduction

The Deprivation of Liberty Safeguards (DoLS) came into force in April 2009 and form part of the Mental Capacity Act 2005 (the Act). The Act is a wide-ranging piece of legislation that governs the care, treatment and finances of adults who lack capacity to consent or make decisions in these areas. The Act is like a book with a series of chapters and paragraphs (known as 'parts' and 'sections' in law) that introduce different powers or procedures. They include:

- Assessing whether a person has capacity
- What is in a person's best interests if they lack capacity
- Advance decisions (often called 'living wills')
- Restraining people who lack capacity to prevent harm to them
- Lasting powers of attorney
- The Court of Protection
- Deprivation of Liberty Safeguards

DoLS is designed to legally authorise restrictive care situations for people who lack capacity to consent to them. The power is only available if the person meets all the DoLS criteria and is in a care home or hospital. For the purposes of this book 'DoLS' is used to refer to the *deprivation of liberty safeguards* and the term 'authorisation' refers to the legal authority to deprive a person of their liberty under DoLS. Anyone under DoLS is given a series of legal rights and protection (see page 4). A person may also be deprived of their liberty in another location such as supported living or a residential school but this requires an order from the Court of Protection (see page 84).

When DoLS was introduced in 2009, its use around the country by care homes and hospitals was limited. In 2013, for example, there were on average only 1,600 people under DoLS on any one day in England. From March 2014, however, a huge change was introduced by the Supreme Court, the highest court of the United Kingdom. The court was asked to rule on whether three people in care were being deprived of their liberty. Previously, lower courts had ruled that although the people concerned had restrictions placed on them (for example they needed another adult to escort them outside to keep them safe) they were not deprived of their liberty. The Supreme Court disagreed and overruled the previous judgments, effectively setting a new and much lower threshold for determining a deprivation of liberty in care settings. At the time of writing (October 2015) the number of people now being assessed as deprived of their liberty in care has risen substantially across England and Wales. The latest government statistics[2] show that for the year April 2014 to March 2015 there were 137,540 DoLS applications received by local authorities in England.

DoLS has been the subject of criticism since its inception. The government's view[3] however is that:

*'DoLS should be regarded ... as a hugely positive tool that shines a light on the circumstances of an individual's care to determine if a deprivation of liberty is necessary to deliver the care envisaged and in the best interests of the individual. In such circumstances, rather than a mark against an organisation it is quite the opposite – a marker of the organisation's respect for the rights of those it cares for and a commitment to put these first at all times.'*

Having said this, the Law Commission, at the request of the government, is currently reviewing DoLS and developing proposals for a less complex statutory procedure[4] nevertheless any replacement however is not expected to come into effect until 2018 at the earliest.

This book is designed to be an accessible and practical guide to DoLS for a range of professionals, care staff and others involved in the procedures. It is not exhaustive and does not include a complete copy of the legislation, regulations, the Code of Practice or case law but rather has extracted key information from each of these to produce what we hope is a comprehensive guide to a complex area of law. We value any comments and suggestions for improving and amending future editions. If you would like write to us please email: *admin@bookswise.org.uk*

Aasya F Mughal and Steven Richards
October 2015

## Deprivation of Liberty Safeguards (DoLS) – Overview

Protection for people who lack capacity to be resident for care or treatment and who have restrictions in place to keep them safe. The restrictions mean the person is under *'complete supervision and control and not free to leave'* and so is deprived of their liberty. DoLS provides a legal means to authorise this.

**Who?**

Any adult aged 18 and over who has a mental disorder and lacks capacity to be resident for care or treatment plus other legal criteria.

The Court of Protection can authorise the deprivation from the age of 16.

**Where?**

Any registered care home or hospital in England or Wales.

If a person is deprived of their liberty in other locations (supported living, extra care or their own home for example) an application to the Court of Protection is needed.

**Legal Bodies**

Managing authorities = care homes and hospitals. Responsible for identifying residents who lack capacity and may be deprived of their liberty.

Supervisory bodies = local authorities and Welsh health boards. Responsible for arranging the assessments for standard authorisations and then authorising them.

**When?**

A person who lacks capacity to be resident for care or treatment and is subject to restrictions to prevent them coming to harm. The restrictions in place mean the person is subject to *'complete supervision and control AND not free to leave'* which means they are deprived of their liberty.

**Assessors**

A minimum of two for standard authorisations. A mental health assessor (doctor) and a DoLS best interests assessor (BIA – a specially trained social worker, nurse, occupational therapist or psychologist).

**How?**

There are two types of DoLS authorisations.

Urgent (7-14 days) – authorised by the care home or hospital themselves for up to 7 days and this can be extended to 14 days with permission from the supervisory body (local authority).

Standard (up to 1 year) – involving independent assessors and authorised by the supervisory body (local authority). The assessment process requires that the views of the person concerned and their family and friends are taken into account and that less restrictive options for care are considered.

**Why?**

DoLS is fundamentally about the human rights of adults and what is meant by the concept of liberty or freedom. The use of DoLS is not a criticism of a care provider. By using DoLS both the person and the care provider are legally protected. The government has stated[3]: *'DoLS should be regarded ... as a hugely positive tool that shines a light on the circumstances of an individual's care ... rather than a mark against an organisation it is quite the opposite – a marker of the organisation's respect for the rights of those it cares for and a commitment to put these first at all times.'*

**Rights**

A person placed under a standard DoLS is given a series of rights including:

Appeal
Review
Representative
Advocacy (IMCA)
CQC monitoring

## Challenges of DoLS

One of the challenges of DoLS for staff who provide care and support to people who lack capacity every day is understanding why a person who is content with where they live, has never tried to leave, is receiving very good care and whose family are happy with the placement could also be assessed as being deprived of their liberty. It is clear from the judgment of the Supreme Court (see page 20) that there is a difference in interpretation between what care homes and hospitals call care and support and what the law classes as restrictions or supervision and control, which lead to a deprivation of liberty. Lady Justice Hale in the Supreme Court ruling[5] stated:

*'It would not be at all surprising if those arranging for the care of people with severe learning disabilities were reluctant to see those arrangements, made in what they think are the best interests of the people concerned, as also depriving them of their liberty. ... We should not confuse the question of the quality of the arrangements which have been made with the question of whether these arrangements constitute a deprivation of liberty.'*

Many people, for very good reasons, need care and support to protect them from coming to harm. For people who can give or refuse consent to such care and support (because they have the mental capacity to do so), DoLS does not apply and is not necessary. However, if a person is not able to consent to such care and support, because they lack the mental capacity to do so, the situation changes and the Mental Capacity Act applies. In such cases it is not uncommon that the care and support provided also mean the person is restricted in what they can and cannot do (for example, they cannot use the kitchen alone because they are unable to operate the equipment there safely). This does not mean the care and support is poor. In many cases it enables the person to do things they could not otherwise do. For people providing care to others it may be useful to consider whether they themselves would feel restricted if, for example, someone told them they could not go outside unless another adult was with them. For the purposes of the legal definition of a deprivation of liberty, the reasons (ie the person's condition) do not matter. What matters is that they are being controlled and supervised and are therefore considered to be deprived of their liberty.

---

### Positive impact of DoLS

Independent research on DoLS by the National Institute of Health Research[6] has found:

- The majority of BIAs felt DoLS had a positive impact on the human rights of the individual.
- DoLS led to detailed scrutiny of care practice.
- Evidence that the DoLS procedure brought about beneficial changes in a person's care.
- Positive reports from relatives regarding the contact they had with BIAs as part of the DoLS assessment providing them with an opportunity to give their views about their relative's care.

The Care Quality Commission in its last annual report on DoLS[7] stated: *'The Deprivation of Liberty Safeguards are set firmly within the empowering ethos of the Mental Capacity Act (MCA). They encourage all health and social care providers to put liberty and autonomy at the heart of care planning, to avoid wherever possible the need to deprive people of their liberty.'*

Health and social care inspectors have found[8]: *'Where Safeguards were in place, they had contributed to supporting people in very challenging circumstances and were particularly effective where there were bespoke conditions aimed at working towards reducing/removing the deprivation.'*

The Minister of State for Community and Social Care, Alistair Burt, has commented[1]: *'Although some may baulk at the idea of 100,000 DOLS applications a year, we should remember that every one of those applications represents a person having their care independently scrutinised. DOLS can help to shine a light on care that is unnecessarily restrictive and does not put the person's views first and foremost. Therefore, we should strongly back the principles of DOLS.'*

## Rights and Protection

DoLS provides a series of rights and protective mechanisms for those affected by it. Many of these are required under the clauses of the European Convention on Human Rights. It is important for assessors, care providers and others affected by DoLS to be informed and aware of them. The table below provides a summary and more detail is given in the pages that follow. For staff in mental health services see page 105 comparing rights under the Mental Health Act with DoLS.

| | |
|---|---|
| **Legal criteria** | The legal criteria for DoLS set a minimum standard that must be met to deprive a person of their liberty. The criteria for DoLS are multi-faceted but perhaps one of the most important is the best interests assessment. This assessment means a number of factors are taken into account including the views of the person concerned, those of their family and less restrictive options (see page 36). |
| **Professional assessors** | Health and social care staff, who have undertaken specialist training to become DoLS assessors, are responsible for assessing whether a person meets the legal criteria for a standard DoLS authorisation (see page 91). |
| **Appeal** | There is a right of appeal to the Court of Protection at any time whilst under DoLS. In addition, the person's representative has the same right of appeal. Other people such as advocates, with permission from the court, are also able to appeal (see page 84). |
| **Review** | A standard DoLS authorisation can be reviewed at any time and this can be requested by a number of different people for various reasons. A review means a professional assessor considers whether the legal criteria of the DoLS are still met (see page 82). |
| **Representative** | Every person under a standard DoLS authorisation has a representative appointed for them. The purpose of the role is to support the person and ensure their rights are protected. They can appeal directly to the Court of Protection (see page 75). |
| **Advocacy** | Every person under DoLS has the right to access an advocate (see page 79). |
| **Conditions** | Every standard DoLS authorisation can have conditions attached by the local authority. These are often designed to improve the care of the person concerned (see page 73). |
| **Informed of rights** | Care homes and hospitals are legally required to inform a person of their rights under DoLS, both verbally and in writing (see page 97). |
| **Copies of assessments** | Copies of all assessments must be given to the person under DoLS and also their representative. This means both are able to see the reasons and evidence for the DoLS and, if they are not satisfied, can challenge it (see page 93). |
| **Flexible duration** | Rather than a standard duration for each individual under DoLS, the local authority can set a date that reflects the view of the assessors about the most appropriate (proportionate) duration. The *maximum* period that may be set for each standard authorisation is 12 months (see page 72). |
| **Care Quality Commission** | The CQC is required to monitor the operation of DoLS. In relation to hospital inspections in England it has recently reported[9]: *'We have seen variable staff understanding of the Mental Capacity Act 2005 (MCA) and the Deprivation of Liberty Safeguards (DoLS). In a number of cases, staff did not understand how they should be applying the requirements of the MCA as a whole, or the DoLS in particular, in their roles.'* |

## Facts and Figures

The latest government statistics[2] show that for the year ending March 2015 there were 137,540 DoLS applications received by local authorities in England. This represents a tenfold increase from the previous year (before the impact of the Supreme Court ruling) of just 13,700 applications. Since the Supreme Court ruling in March 2014 the number of applications received by local authorities each month has increased from 4,100 in March 2014 to 13,000 in March 2015. It is not clear when the peak will be reached. (The latest available figures for Wales relate to 2013-14, prior to the Supreme Court ruling, and are therefore not included in this section).

The increase in applications has naturally led to an increase in the number of completed DoLS applications (where DoLS assessments have been completed and a standard authorisation granted or not).

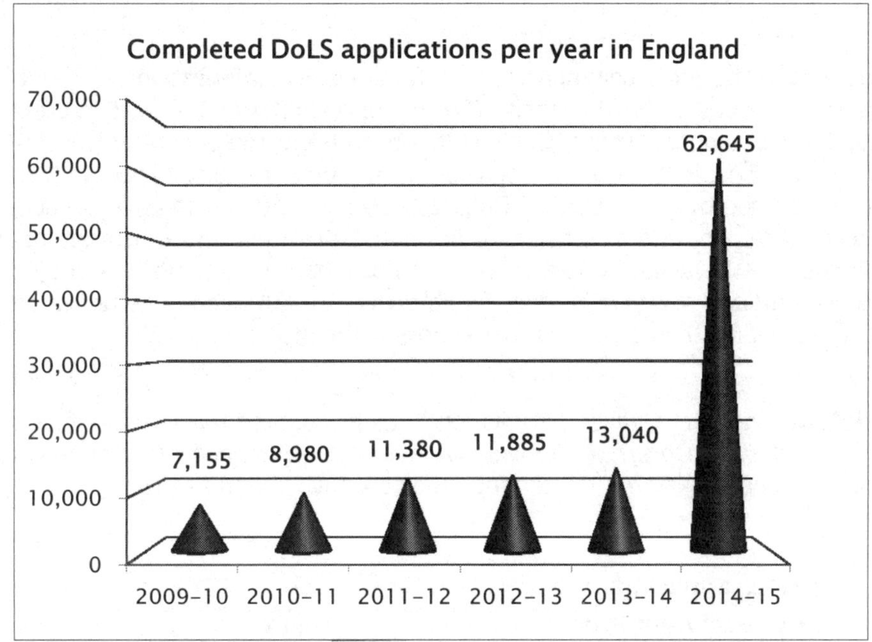


On 31st March 2015 there were 36,216 adults under standard DoLS authorisations. This figure can be expected to increase significantly in the future.

**Gender:** 61% of DoLS applications were for women and 39% for men.

**Age:** 80% of applications were for people aged 65 or over. 40% of all applications were for people aged 85 or over.

**Mental disorder:** 51% of people were diagnosed with dementia with the next largest group being learning disability (14%).

**Ethnicity:** 91% of people were from a white ethnic background. This signifies an over representation of this grouping compared to the general population of 85%. This may be explained by cultural differences in the care of older people living in care homes.

**Applications awaiting assessment:** The huge rise in applications following the Supreme Court ruling has overwhelmed local authorities' abilities to carry out assessments speedily. Figures for the end of March 2015 show that over 40% of applications received (approximately 55,000) had not yet been assessed due to the backlog that had built up across England.

---

**Result of DoLS assessments:** For the applications that were assessed and a decision reached, 83% were confirmed and authorised by local authorities so a standard authorisation was granted. This 'conversion' rate from referral to completed assessment shows variation across the country.

---

**Duration of completed authorisations:** The majority of completed DoLS authorisations lasted for less than three months (62%) and only 15% lasted for a period of six months or more. This may be because the DoLS authorisation was not granted for a long duration or because circumstances changed to end the DoLS (for example a review took place or the person concerned died).

---

**Failed assessments:** The most common reasons for a DoLS authorisation not being granted was either the person was found to have capacity (2,895 applications) or the best interests assessment was not met (2,525 applications). These simple statistics highlight the benefit of the DoLS assessment process showing that people who were considered by some to lack capacity (hence the DoLS application) once assessed by a professional DoLS assessor were found to have capacity to make the decision regarding placement in a care home or hospital. In relation to the best interests criteria not being met, this could be because the restrictions did not mean the person was subject to *complete supervision and control and not free to leave* or otherwise that the care was not appropriate to the person's needs which would then trigger further action by the local authority.

---

**Regional variation:** The Care Quality Commission[10] has highlighted this issue in its annual review of DoLS: *'A source of ongoing concern is the wide variations in application rates by region.'* The latest statistics for the year ending March 2015 continue to show such variation.

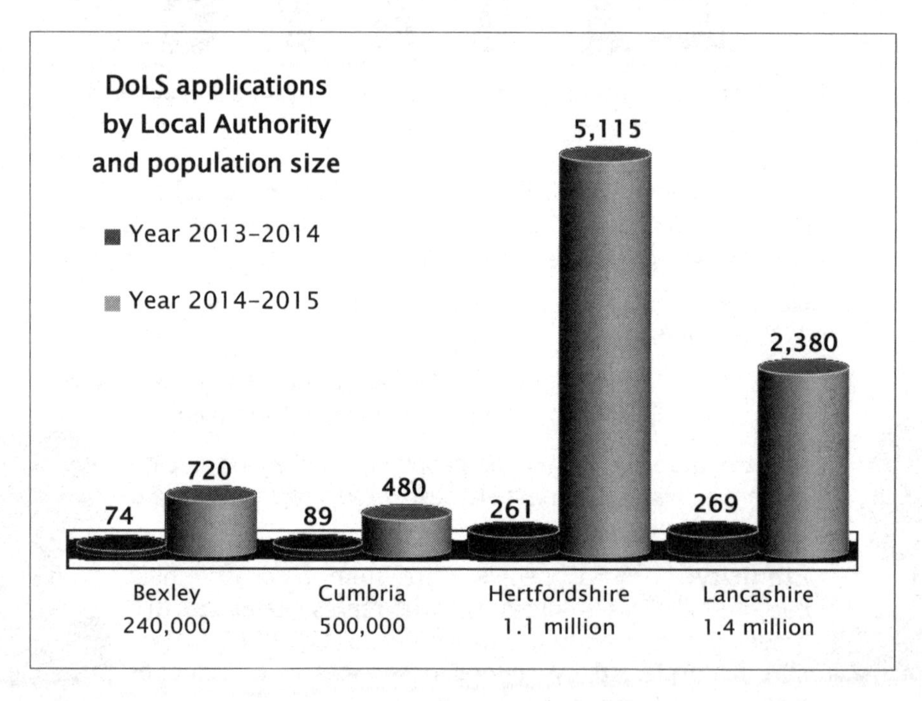


The official statistics note: *'The North East has the highest rate of applications by far, with 389 applications per 100,000 residents. This is more than double the next highest region, the North West. The other eight regions still display relatively wide variation ...'*

All of the figures in this chapter were taken from the Health & Social Care Information Centre: *Mental Capacity Act (2005) Deprivation of Liberty Safeguards (England) Annual Report 2014-15* available from: *www.hscic.gov.uk.*

## Guidance

There is a legal hierarchy in DoLS guidance and the list below shows how courts consider cases brought to them.

1. **European Convention on Human Rights**
   This is where the need for the DoLS process originates. Article 5 of the Convention gives every adult the right to liberty. However this right can be taken away in certain circumstances. Where a person is subject to restrictions which they have not consented to, this can mean they are deprived of their liberty and a legal procedure is required to authorise this. The state (government authorities) is not allowed to deprive a person of their liberty unless they meet certain legal criteria and give the person a right to appeal.

2. **European Court of Human Rights judgments**
   The court cannot re-write the Convention but its role is to interpret, through different appeals that come to it, what being 'free' or conversely being 'deprived of liberty' means in practice. For example if a person goes out alone every day from a care home but they are told and expected to return by 5pm, does this mean they are deprived of their liberty?

3. **Domestic legislation – Deprivation of Liberty Safeguards or DoLS**
   This is our own domestic legislation which the government introduced in April 2009 in response to an earlier European Court of Human Rights ruling where the court found a gap in our law. In the case (informally known as the 'Bournewood case') the European Court found a person who lacked capacity had been unlawfully deprived of his liberty and the UK did not have a system in place to authorise it and guarantee the person's rights.

4. **Case law – court rulings about DoLS**
   Our courts cannot rewrite domestic legislation but they can interpret its meaning and application. This has been of fundamental importance in DoLS as the domestic legislation did not define deprivation of liberty in a care setting so it has been the courts' role through individual cases to provide the definition. The Supreme Court ruled in March 2014 on three people in care and effectively created a new (much lower) threshold for considering when a person is deprived of their liberty. This ruling is the fundamental benchmark for assessing whether a person is deprived of their liberty in care settings.

5. **Code of Practice**
   DoLS has a statutory Code of Practice which is designed to provide practical guidance for staff and others in relation to the safeguards. There is a legal duty on professionals and paid staff working with people who lack capacity to '*have regard to*' the guidance within it (see page 124). It is important to note that following the Supreme Court's ruling in Cheshire West, the Code's chapter on what care constitutes a deprivation of liberty is no longer a reliable guide on this particular issue.

6. **Professional guidance**
   At the time of writing, the most recent and authoritative guide to care situations that may or may not be a deprivation of liberty is the Law Society's guidance[11]. The Department of Health, the Social Care Institute of Excellence (SCIE), the Care Quality Commission (CQC) and other organisations also produce useful information. However, in terms of legal hierarchy, they all have less weight than the sources listed above and any case law that contradicts the guidance at this level will override it.

   The main government website for approved information on the Mental Capacity Act and DoLS is: www.scie.org.uk/mca-directory.

## The Principles

The Mental Capacity Act has five principles which apply to all parts of the legislation including DoLS. These are the foundations of the entire legislation and everyone using the Act must follow them. The principles can be seen as a set of rights for people whose mental capacity is called into question and as they are statutory requirements, the failure to follow them can be referred to in the course of legal proceedings. The principles are:

**When assessing capacity:**

1. A person must be assumed to have capacity UNLESS it is proved otherwise.
2. All practicable steps must be taken to help someone make a decision before they can be assessed as lacking capacity.
3. An unwise decision does NOT in itself indicate a lack of capacity.

**When acting or making decisions on behalf of someone lacking capacity:**

4. Any act or decision made must be in the person's best interests.
5. Any act or decision should aim to be the less restrictive option available in terms of the person's rights and freedom of action.

**Principle 1**: *A person must be assumed to have capacity unless it is proved otherwise.*

This means that all people (aged 16+) must be assumed to have capacity regardless of their condition (learning disability, dementia, brain injury etc), behaviour or residence (in hospital or residential care). The burden of proof as to whether someone lacks capacity falls on those assessing the person. If staff think that a person does not have capacity to make a decision on a matter, the Act requires that they provide evidence of this. This evidence comes from completing the capacity assessment, which the legislation lays out in Sections 2 and 3 (page 47). If there is insufficent evidence of incapacity, the assessor *must* conclude the person has capacity. If the case is serious and there are doubts either way, legal advice and ultimately an application to the Court of Protection may be considered for a judge to decide on the person's mental capacity.

---

**Principle 2**: *All practicable steps must be taken to help someone make a decision before they can be assessed as lacking capacity.*

This is a positive legal obligation on those assessing a person's capacity to help and support someone they consider to lack capacity during the assessment process. The aim of this is to assist the person to pass the assessment so they can make their own decision. Again, evidence of providing help and support will need to be shown. What constitutes a practicable step will depend on the circumstances of each case. For example, the time available will have an impact on what is practicable, so care provided in an emergency will limit the steps it is possible to take to assist a person with the assessment process. Outside of emergency care, practical steps could include giving a person more time so they are able to make a decision or assisting the person to understand the information using pictures or a translator.

---

**Principle 3**: *An unwise decision does not in itself indicate a lack of capacity.*

The Act enforces the established legal principle that adults with capacity are entitled to make, what others may view as, irrational or eccentric decisions. The Supreme Court in the case of *Aintree University Hospitals NHS Foundation Trust v James [2013] UKSC 67,* stated: *'Every adult capable of making decisions has an absolute right to accept or refuse medical treatment, regardless of the wisdom or consequences of the decision. The decision does not have to be justified to anyone. Without consent any invasion of the body, however well-meaning or therapeutic, will be criminal assault.'*

The key issue is whether the person has capacity to make the decision (which includes an understanding and acceptance of the consequences of their decision) which is determined by the capacity assessment in the legislation.

In society, many people with full mental capacity make decisions that others may view as 'unwise' but cannot be prevented from doing so. For example, some people decide to drink excessively, eat a very unhealthy diet, smoke or perhaps take part in dangerous activities. Some people refuse medical treatment perhaps due to their religious beliefs. The law upholds an individual's right to do this as long as they have the mental capacity to understand and accept the consequences of their choice. If people take part in criminal activities, criminal law can be used to deal with them.

---

**Principle 4**: *Any act or decision (health, social care or financial) for someone lacking capacity must be made in their best interests.*

The term '*best interests'* is expanded upon in the legislation under Section 4, which provides a checklist to follow when deciding what is in a person's best interests (see page 56). This checklist only becomes applicable when making decisions for those who lack capacity. If the person has capacity, they will make their own decisions.

---

**Principle 5**: *When a person lacks capacity, any act or decision (health, social care or financial) should aim to be the less restrictive option available to the person in terms of their rights and freedom of action.*

This is a positive obligation on those making a decision in a person's best interests to consider less restrictive options. The MCA Code of Practice (para 2.14) notes that people making decisions: ' ... *must always question if they can do something else that would interfere less with the person's basic rights and freedoms.*'

The Act requires consideration of this but in some cases it may not be possible to follow a less restrictive option. Examples of less restrictive options could include less restrictive medication or surgery (perhaps with fewer side effects) or the location of accommodation chosen (perhaps a placement in a care home which is closest to family and friends) or the type of care package given (supporting a person in their own home as opposed to placing them in a care home).

- *Question: Can budgetary constraints be taken into account when considering the less restrictive option?*

It is inevitable that some best interest decisions will be limited due to financial resources. Indeed, the Act does not dictate a minimal amount of money to be spent when best interest decisions are made and the Act (or the Court of Protection) has no authority to force a more expensive option to be chosen. Indeed, recent case law (see page 57) has shown that the Court of Protection rather than forcing a more expensive option may decide not to authorise a deprivation of liberty if it believes less restrictive options have not been adequately pursued. Financial decisions made by local authorities can be challenged through alternative legal processes such as an application for judicial review.

# The Mental Capacity Act and DoLS

The Act governs the care and treatment of people aged 16 and over who lack capacity, because of an impairment of or disturbance in the functioning of the mind or brain, to consent to care or treatment. DoLS, as one part of the Act, fits into its general structure as follows:

**Assessment of Capacity**

The Act is founded on the concept of whether people have mental capacity to make their own decisions.

- An assessment of capacity is time and decision specific.
- To have capacity a person must, at a specific time and for a specific decision, be able to 1. Understand 2. Retain 3. Use/Weigh 4. Communicate a decision (see page 47 for more detail).
- If they cannot do one of the above points *because of* an impairment of or disturbance in the functioning of the mind or brain they would be assessed as lacking capacity.

**Best Interests**

If a person lacks capacity nothing can be done to or for them unless it is in their best interests.

Best interests under the Act means consideration of a statutory checklist of items which includes:

the relevant circumstances + current and prior wishes of the person + beliefs and values of the person + consulting people who know the person + less restrictive options in delivering care + including the person + considering whether the person is likely to regain capacity (see page 56 for more detail).

**Restraint**

The Act defines restraint as: the use or threat of force to make a person do something they resist *or* the restriction of liberty of movement whether or not the person resists.

Criteria for use: a person lacks capacity about the proposed act + the proposed act is in their best interests + the restraint is to prevent harm to them + the restraint is a proportionate response to the risk and likelihood of harm.

Under the Act, any person can restrain someone lacking capacity in any place as long as the criteria above are met (see page 11 for more detail).

**Deprivation of Liberty Safeguards**

- To protect some people who lack capacity from coming to harm the level of restrictions/restraint needed falls into the category of also depriving the person of their liberty.
- DoLS covers people in care homes or hospitals but if a person is anywhere else the Court of Protection can authorise the deprivation of liberty.

Any actions to treat or care for people under DoLS need mental capacity assessments and best interests assessments for that specific act.

## **Restraint** (Section 6 of the Mental Capacity Act)

Many people who lack capacity to consent to care provision are restricted in some way in order to keep them safe. The key question in DoLS is whether the restrictions in place amount to a deprivation of liberty. The starting point therefore in discussing DoLS is to look at how the Act defines restraint. This is especially important as the legal criteria for DoLS mirrors the criteria used for restraint in the Act. The power of restraint is certainly not new having been used for centuries in institutions providing care and treatment. However, the Act clarifies earlier common law powers to ensure that, if properly followed, both the person carrying out the restraint and the person being restrained are adequately protected by the law.

Restraint is important because it means that a person who lacks capacity is not left without necessary care or treatment because they do not understand what is happening. For example, a person with a learning disability may not understand the need for an injection and consequently may not hold their arm still. A minimal amount of restraint may be used to keep them still for the duration of the procedure. This would mean they would not go without a necessary vaccination or perhaps a diagnostic test such as a blood test.

---

### Definition of restraint

Restraint within the Mental Capacity Act is defined as:

> the use or threat of using force to make a person do something they are resisting
> **or**
> the restriction of liberty of movement, whether or not the person resists

Within this definition restraint could be: verbal and may involve threatening a person with restraint; chemical such as sedation; physical such as holding a person, preventing them leaving a place (temporarily) by using locked doors or restricting a person's ability to move freely (lap belts). Even minor acts may restrict liberty of movement. Care providers should ensure their policies recognise this statutory definition of restraint and review their procedures to take this into account.

---

### Criteria needed for restraint

Only by following the criteria below are staff empowered to restrain a person under the legislation and protected in law for the actions they take:

1. The person lacks capacity in relation to the matter in question and it will be in the person's best interests for the act to be done
   **and**
2. It is reasonable to believe that it is necessary to restrain the person to prevent harm to them
   **and**
3. The restraint is a proportionate response to the likelihood of the person suffering harm and the seriousness of that harm.

### 1. Lacks mental capacity and in the person's best interests

This means that an assessment of capacity has been carried out and the person has been found to lack capacity in relation to the particular matter, and a best interests assessment has confirmed that it is in their best interests for the particular action to be taken. For example, the person lacks mental capacity consent to an injection and it is in their best interests for the injection to be given to them. In an emergency situation, these assessments may be done very quickly and recorded after the restraint has taken place.

## 2. Necessary to prevent harm to them

Restraint under the Act may only be used to prevent harm to the person lacking capacity who is to be restrained. The MCA Code of Practice (para 6.45) gives the following examples of harm:

1. *'a person with learning disabilities might run into a busy road without warning, if they do not understand the dangers of cars*
2. *a person with dementia may wander away from home and get lost, if they cannot remember where they live*
3. *a person with manic depression might engage in excessive spending during a manic phase, causing them to get into debt*
4. *a person may also be at risk of harm if they behave in a way that encourages others to assault or exploit them (for example, by behaving in a dangerously provocative way).'*

---

## 3. A proportionate response

A proportionate response is one that represents the minimum force necessary for the shortest possible time. The onus falls on the person carrying out the restraint to identify the reasons which justify it. The MCA Code of Practice (para 6.47) notes: *'... a carer may need to hold a person's arm while they cross the road, if the person does not understand the dangers of roads. But it would not be a proportionate response to stop the person going outdoors at all. It may be appropriate to have a secure lock on a door that faces a busy road, but it would not be a proportionate response to lock someone in a bedroom all the time to prevent them from attempting to cross the road.'*

---

### Recording restraint

The Act does not provide a form to record the use of restraint. However, staff would need to document that they had followed the criteria of the Act as given above in either the person's case notes or on any forms created by their organisation for this purpose. In a recent court case *(AJ v A local authority [2015] EWCOP 5)* a judge stated the following relating to the care of an older woman with dementia in a care home:

*'... in any case in which physical restraint is used in the care of an incapacitated adult, any physical intervention, whether considered to amount to 'restraint' or not, should be recorded in the care plan maintained by the service provider and monitored by the statutory body responsible for commissioning the person's care. Furthermore, precise details of all physical interventions should be ascertained and documented as part of the Deprivation of Liberty Safeguards process or indeed any best interest assessment from direct discussion with care staff implementing the interventions.'*

---

### Who can carry out restraint?

Anybody providing care to people who lack capacity could use the power of restraint. There is no requirement in the Act that anyone undertaking restraint should be specifically trained in physical restraint techniques. For example, family may restrain someone to some extent every time they are washed. A court would expect much higher standards of training and procedure from a professional organisation compared with family carers. See the case of: *The Mental Health Trust & Ors v DD & Anor [2015] EWCOP 4*, paragraph 136.

---

### Where can the power of restraint be used?

The Act does not limit the locations in which restraint may be undertaken. As long as the criteria are met the restraint could be carried out anywhere.

---

### Reviewing restraint

Once restraint is authorised, the power should be kept under review to ensure it is being used properly. Although restraint may be permitted, staff should consider if other less restrictive and more proportionate actions could be taken. Staff should also consider whether the restraint is still in the person's best interests.

**Lasting powers of attorney**

If it is within their authority (health and welfare), an attorney may restrain a person or authorise someone else to restrain the person if the criteria under the Act are met. An attorney cannot however authorise a deprivation of liberty.

---

**Court appointed deputies**

A deputy can restrain a person if the criteria are met *and* they have authority for restraint conferred on them by the Court of Protection. A deputy may also authorise someone else to restrain the person. A deputy cannot however authorise a deprivation of liberty.

---

**Prior instructions on restraint**

If a person has a lasting power of attorney or there is a court appointed deputy whose scope of authority covers this area and either the attorney or deputy have given prior instructions, these cannot be overridden. However, if the attorney's or deputy's instructions would stop a person receiving life-sustaining treatment or lead to a serious deterioration in their condition, then the staff involved could treat the person whilst an urgent decision is sought from the Court of Protection.

---

**Restraint v deprivation of liberty**

The power of restraint permits the use or threat of force to make a person do something they are resisting or authorises the restriction of liberty of movement, whether or not the person resists, if certain criteria are met. However it does NOT permit any act that *deprives* a person of their liberty (as opposed to *restricts* their liberty). This is where the separate power of DoLS must be used.

---

***Question:*** *I have a client with a learning disability and challenging behaviour. They need regular eye drops to prevent them going blind. They lack capacity regarding the need for the drops and when we try to give them, they resist. Could we restrain them to give the eye drops?*

Yes, as long as the criteria of the Act are met, proportionate restraint could be used. Staff would be protected for the actions they take to carry out the restraint and the person lacking capacity would be protected from coming to harm.

***Question:*** *I work in a day centre for people with dementia. We have one client at present, who often tries to leave the centre. If he went out he would be at risk of harm as we are near a busy road. We have tried distraction but it does not always work and we either need to hold him to prevent him leaving or lock the centre doors for a short time. However, our policy says we cannot use restraint at the day centre, what should we do?*

The policy of the day centre is wrong in law. The Act has greater authority than a policy and the example above would meet the legal criteria of restraint (restricting liberty of movement) if other means of distraction failed and restraint represented a proportionate response to protect the person from harm. If the person was not restrained and therefore came to harm (by being allowed to leave the day centre) staff would not be protected by the legislation.

***Question:*** *Does the wording 'harm to themselves' include psychological harm?*

Neither the Act nor the Code of Practice defines harm and they do not refer to psychological harm. However the courts have cited the management of anxiety (using Risperidone) as meeting this definition (*P & Q v Surrey County Council [2011] EWCA Civ 190).*

***Question:*** *What about situations where the harm is to other people?*

Restraint under the Act (and also DoLS) cannot be used to prevent harm to others. That said, clearly staff have a duty of care to all people for whom they provide services and there are common law powers of restraint if a person (regardless of their capacity) is acting in a way that will cause harm to others. Staff may, under common law, take appropriate and necessary (reasonable) actions to restrain the person to prevent harm to others or themselves.

## Deprivation of Liberty – A Legal Summary

**European Convention on Human Rights**
*Article 5: every person has the right to liberty and security of person*

This right is not unlimited and a person can however be deprived of their liberty in certain circumstances. For a person to prove they have been deprived of their liberty under Article 5, three elements must be present.

**The objective element**
The person is confined in a particular place for an extended (not negligible) period of time. This is often referred to as the *concrete situation.*

**The subjective element**
No consent. Either because the person has not consented to, or lacks capacity (DoLS requirement) to consent to, the control placed on them.

**The state element**
The deprivation of liberty may be blamed on the state (NHS, local authority, CCG, CQC etc) either directly or indirectly.

**Guzzardi Assessment**
Taken from the case of *Guzzardi v Italy [1980] 3 EHRR* this is a standardised method to assess the objective element. The concrete situation (care plan) of the person is assessed in terms of the actual restrictions in place. Each restriction is considered in terms of type, duration, effect, manner of implementation and the degree or intensity of the restriction. The cumulative effect of the restrictions should also be considered.

**Supreme Court ruling 'Cheshire West'**
Having analysed the restrictions in the care plan using the Guzzardi assessment do you consider the person is under:

*'complete supervision and control* ***and*** *not free to leave'*

**Authorisation of deprivation of liberty**
If the answer above is YES, the person is under *'complete supervision and control and not free to leave'* they are deprived of their liberty. This must be authorised either by:

**1. DoLS** – person aged 18 or over in a care home or hospital
**2. Court of Protection** – person aged 16 in other locations
**3. The Mental Health Act 1983** – person on a mental health ward for treatment of their mental disorder (see page 105 for more detail)

(Note: The Children Act can also be applied (see page116) and in exceptional cases when no other powers are available the High Court can independently authorise a deprivation of liberty by giving a court order (inherent jurisdiction))

## Deprivation of Liberty – The Legal Context

We all have the right to be free. Article 5 of the European Convention on Human Rights (ECHR) sets out and safeguards this basic human right. However, the right to freedom (or liberty) is not without limitation. For example, the right to be free may be taken away if a person has been found guilty of committing a crime and is sentenced to a term of imprisonment. What is important is that if a person's freedom is taken away, the law is used to do this. Furthermore, the person should be given the right to appeal.

When it comes to DoLS the reason for the loss of a person's freedom or liberty is altogether different. In these circumstances a care home or hospital that needs to protect someone who is either already in, or will be in their care uses DoLS to provide them with the legal authority to care for that person, supervise them and stop them leaving because the person has not been able to consent to this. These actions also mean that the person subject to such supervision or oversight cannot be described as a free individual. The supervision and control which is protecting the person mean they have had their liberty taken away; they are *deprived of their liberty.*

Whilst DoLS gives a care home or hospital the authority to take away a person's liberty, it also gives the resident or patient, being looked after in this way, rights. Instead of being kept in the care home or hospital without the opportunity to challenge this decision through law (as often happened in the past), under DoLS the person may go to court or ask for a review by independent assessors.

Many people will argue that such care should not be described as a deprivation of liberty; that the care and control is simply in the person's best interests. DoLS does not change the fact that some people should be in care homes and hospitals with supervision and control. It merely makes it legal. It offers the resident or patient legal rights and it protects the care home or hospital by giving them legal authority to keep a person, who has not consented, under supervision and control and stop them leaving. Just as the Mental Health Act 1983 is often used to deprive people of their liberty and keep them safe, so is the Mental Capacity Act (which encompasses DoLS) also employed.

---

### Deprivation of Liberty – Article 5 European Convention on Human Rights

Article 5 of the European Convention on Human Rights sets out the right to liberty and security:

*'Everyone has the right to liberty and security of person. No one shall be deprived of his liberty save in the following cases and in accordance with a procedure prescribed by law ... Everyone who is deprived of his liberty by arrest or detention shall be entitled to take proceedings by which the lawfulness of his detention shall be decided speedily by a court and his release ordered if the detention is not lawful.'*

The *cases* referred to in the above passage include those who have a mental disorder. Essentially Article 5 requires any deprivation of liberty to follow a *'procedure prescribed by law'* and gives the person the right to go to court and disagree with the decision to take away their liberty.

**Note:** DoLS provides authority to deprive a person of their liberty. It does NOT provide permission for a local authority to limit contact with family or prevent a person living with their family. Such actions affect a person's private and family life (Article 8 ECHR) and require authority from the Court of Protection (see page 84).

---

### The three elements

European case law has established that for a person to be deprived of their liberty, three elements must be present. These are known as:

- the **objective** element > a person is confined to a particular place
- the **subjective** element > they have not consented to this
- imputable to the **state** > the state is involved

**Subjective element** (lack of consent)

The person being deprived of their liberty cannot have *consented* to the restrictions placed upon them. In DoLS, the absence of consent is because the person lacks the mental capacity. This is assessed by the mental capacity assessment undertaken as part of the DoLS criteria. The assessment requires a confirmation that the person to be subject to DoLS lacks the mental capacity to consent to stay in a care home or hospital for the purpose of being given the care and/or treatment they require.

**Imputable to the state** (the state is involved)

The state (local authority, NHS, CCG or other body) must be responsible in some way for the actions which resulted in the deprivation of liberty. The deprivation of liberty is then said to be 'imputable to the state'. Imputable is another way of saying that the actions may be attributed to the state. This would normally be because the local authority or NHS had been involved in placing a person in a care home or hospital or were paying for some part of the care package. However, the state may also be indirectly responsible because it is either partially organising a person's care, or the person is being cared for in a placement registered by the state (CQC registered).

Private care arrangements delivered in the domestic home are an evolving area of case law and readers should seek further advice on individual cases. If the state is not involved in any way, and cannot reasonably know about a person being deprived of their liberty, then technically there cannot be a deprivation liberty under human rights law. However an organisation undertaking carers assessments on behalf of a local authority (under the Care Act 2014) could be informed by a carer about how the person they care for is restricted to keep them from coming to harm and this could be enough to trigger this element of deprivation of liberty.

**Objective Element** (restrictions amount to a deprivation of liberty)

This is satisfied if a person has been confined (restricted) for a 'not negligible' period of time. What period of time is considered 'not negligible' will depend on the intensity of control in the person's case. Generally, the more intense the control, the sooner the threshold is crossed.

This element means looking at the person's specific circumstances and assessing the restrictions they are subject to. In each case where a deprivation of liberty has been in question, a court has had to do this. It is sometimes referred to as assessing the person's '*concrete situation*'. Broadly, this would include looking at the person's care plan and the length of time for which they are controlled, which restrictions they are under and overall, how intense this is or to what degree this is limiting their freedom.

The most recent legal position means that if someone who *lacks mental capacity* to consent is placed in a care home or hospital and they are under *complete supervision and control and are not free to leave* that placement, they are deprived of their liberty.

See the following pages for more detail on this part of deprivation of liberty.

### The objective element

This requires the assessor to look at the actual situation the person is in and the restrictions applied to them and assess whether they are significant enough to amount to a deprivation of liberty. For over 30 years, the way in which the courts, including the Supreme Court in *Cheshire West* identified the objective element is by reference to a range of factors set out in the case of *Guzzardi v Italy [1980] 3 EHRR*. The range of factors described in the Guzzardi case were:

| **Type + Duration + Effect + Manner + Degree or Intensity** |
|---|

The circumstances of this case were very different to DoLS cases (it scrutinised whether the decision to require Mr Guzzardi to stay on the island of Asinara, off the coast of Sardinia, in order to prevent him from engaging in Mafia activities, amounted to a deprivation of his liberty). Nonetheless, the Supreme Court judgment in Cheshire West noted the importance of the Guzzardi case: '... [it] *is right to say that the Guzzardi test is repeated in all the cases, irrespective of context. If any of these cases went to Strasbourg, we could confidently predict that it would be repeated once more.'* This prediction has proven true as in a recent (2015) judgment *(Stankov v Bulgaria [2015] Application No. 25820/07)* the European Court of Human Rights ruling on whether a man with a mental disorder was deprived of his liberty in a care home stated: '...*whether a person has been deprived of his liberty must be based on the actual situation and take into account a set of criteria specific to the particular case as to type, duration, effects and manner of execution of the measures concerned.'*

It is an assessment of the combination of these factors that decides whether a person has been restricted to a degree that deprives them of their liberty.

| **Type** + Duration + Effect + Manner + Degree or Intensity |
|---|

The type of restrictions being applied must be taken into account. Examples include:

- Chemical restraint (sedation or other medication that controls or manages behaviour)
- Physical restraint (holding a person, or moving a person somewhere)
- Restricted access to the outside (locked doors or escorted when outside)
- Restricted choices in terms of lifestyle (activities, clothing, food, where to live)
- Restricted movement within the care home or hospital (the kitchen is locked)
- Telecare (if it limits a person's freedoms)

Restrictions can therefore take various forms:

1. Direct actions – such as physical restraint
2. What if restrictions – what would staff do if a person stopped washing or tried to leave?
3. Restricted access – for example restricted access to a kitchen (locked)

| Type + **Duration** + Effect + Manner + Degree or Intensity |
|---|

Temporary actions that are immediately necessary to prevent harm are unlikely to deprive a person of their liberty. However, the period of time involved cannot be quantified in a number of minutes or hours. The case of *ZH v The Commissioner of Police for the Metropolis [2013] EWCA Civ 69* involved a short period which still amounted to a deprivation of liberty. In this case, just 40 minutes was long enough because of the intensity of the restrictions applied to a young man with a learning disability by a number of police officers using physical restraints and a police vehicle to hold him. This case is an example of how the *type* of restrictions combined with their *degree and intensity* in addition to the *effect* on the individual involved meant that even restrictions of a short duration were found by the courts to result in a deprivation of liberty. The Law Society guidance[11] on identifying deprivation of liberty states that restrictions (where a person is under complete supervision and control and not free to leave) lasting more than 2 to 3 days will usually lead to a deprivation of liberty.

Type + Duration + **Effect** + Manner + Degree or Intensity

The effect that restrictions have on the individual is also an important consideration. For example there could be two people living in a care home who have to be escorted when they go out. One person is happy to be escorted outside and feels safer so it means they actually go out more often than they had previously. The effect of the restriction (escorted outside) is not significant for them. The other person however does not like having an escort with them and finds it distressing to be 'followed' around. As a result they do not want to go out very often. The effect is quite different for each one. Furthermore, if someone with this restriction has family and friends who can escort them out the effect may not be as significant. Indeed, they may go out as much as they did before living in a care home. However, for another person with no family or friends and with few staff able to take them out, the effect is that they might go out far less than before they were admitted to the care home.

Type + Duration + Effect + **Manner** + Degree or Intensity

The manner of the implementation of restrictions is also important. Restrictions that are put in place without consulting other relevant people (such as family or friends) and with no negotiation could be seen as making the control and supervision unnecessarily more intense. Blanket restrictions applied to all care home or hospital residents can present a particular problem in this respect as this would mean they were not individually assessed in terms of need or risk.

Type + Duration + Effect + Manner + **Degree or Intensity**

The final element to assess is the degree or intensity of each restriction and also the overall degree or intensity of the restrictions when considered cumulatively. The question of degree or intensity can determine whether circumstances amount to a restriction or a deprivation of liberty. For example, if the front door of a care home is locked but a resident is free to go out whenever they want and wherever they want, the actual restriction would not have been used with any significant intensity or degree. However they are highly likely to still be deprived of their liberty if they cannot discharge themselves.

---

**Applying the Guzzardi factors**

If all of the factors above are brought together and applied to one restriction, locked doors, the following emerges:

- The **type** of restraint, locked doors, is a physical restraint preventing a person leaving.
- The **duration** of the restraint may be permanent if the doors are always locked.
- The **effect** of the doors being locked on a person will vary enormously depending on whether the person is allowed out (with or without an escort) and if visitors are able to see them. If there are limited escorts the effect will be the person rarely goes out.
- The **manner** of implementation relates to whether the person or their family are consulted and involved in the decision. Although the decision to lock doors is often a blanket action for all residents of a care home, the manner of its implementation would relate to how each resident is assessed for their ability to go outside and that this is kept under review.
- The **degree or intensity** will relate to whether the person is allowed through the doors regularly in some manner (unescorted or escorted) which would lessen the impact of the restriction.

Note: Even when doors are not locked and a person has unescorted leave they can still be deprived of their liberty if the leave is controlled by staff and they were not allowed to discharge themselves.

For the majority of people who lack capacity to be resident for care there will often be a number of different restrictions in their care plan. Each restriction should be assessed in relation to type, duration, effect, manner and degree or intensity. The cumulative effect of the different restrictions in a person's care plan may mean a person is under *complete supervision and control and not free to leave* and therefore deprived of their liberty.

***Question:*** *Why assess the Guzzardi factors when nearly everyone who lacks capacity and is in a care home will be deprived of their liberty because of the Supreme Court ruling?*

The Supreme Court ruling means that for a person who lacks capacity, just a few restrictions of, what might be a fairly low degree or intensity can still mean they are considered to be deprived of their liberty. The Guzzardi factors still need to be assessed because:

1. They provide the evidence of the control and supervision being exercised and therefore a deprivation of liberty. The latest version of the DoLS forms based on the most recent case law and approved by the Department of Health and Association of Directors of Adult Social Services indicate these factors are part of the record required.

2. The BIA, as part of their assessment, needs to confirm the deprivation of liberty is in the person's best interests. This assessment requires them to have a clear understanding of the type, duration, effect, manner and intensity of restrictions in place in order to consider whether the care being delivered is appropriate to the person's needs and the restrictions in the care plan are proportionate.

---

**Medication as a restriction**

Medication which has the effect of restricting a person's freedom of movement or managing their behaviour will constitute a restriction. Referring to the administration of antipsychotic medication (risperidone) to control anxiety, Lord Justice Wilson in the Court of Appeal stated:

*'In my view the administration to a person of medication, at any rate of antipsychotic drugs and other tranquilisers, is always a pointer towards the existence of the objective element: for it suppresses her liberty to express herself as she would otherwise wish. Indeed, if the administration of it is attended by force, its relevance is increased. Furthermore, in that objections may be highly relevant, medication which has the effect of suppressing them may be relevant to an equally high degree.'*

*P & Q v Surrey County Council [2011] EWCA Civ 190*

The court considered such medication restrictive and therefore it concluded it should be included in the consideration of restrictions in the woman's care plan. This does not mean that the administration of such drugs automatically leads to a deprivation of liberty but rather they represent a restriction, just as needing an escort outside is a restriction. In an earlier case *G v E, A Local Authority & F [2010] EWHC 621* the medication, Haloperidol was referred to as one of the restrictions leading to a deprivation of liberty. Other non-antipsychotic medications used to manage behaviour (such as benzodiazepines) could also be considered restrictive.

Significant numbers of people with dementia and learning disability who lack capacity are prescribed medication to manage behavioural issues. In 2009 the Department of Health estimated that 180,000 people with dementia were being prescribed antipsychotic medication, the vast majority of whom did not have psychosis[12]. The report was highly critical of such prescribing and the government promised action to radically reduce the numbers of people with dementia being prescribed antipsychotic medication. For people with a learning disability, the most recent research by NHS England[13] has found that up to 35,000 adults are being prescribed an antipsychotic or an antidepressant (or both) without the appropriate clinical indications required. The use of such medication to manage behaviour is of considerable concern to NHS England[13] which has stated there is now: '*...robust evidence of inappropriate use of powerful medicines in people with learning disabilities. This is not acceptable practice and must improve.'*

BIAs who find this type of prescribing during assessments can, if they feel it is appropriate, propose a condition about medication is attached to the completed standard DoLS authorisation. This could be a requirement that the care home requests a medication review from the prescriber or for hospitals the medication is reviewed by the consultant in charge (see page 73).

## **Supreme Court Judgment in Cheshire West** (the *Acid Test)*

The huge increase in the number of people considered to be deprived of their liberty in care homes, hospitals and other settings is because of the Supreme Court ruling known as *Cheshire West* which was released on 19 March 2014. The full title was:

*P (by his litigation friend the Official Solicitor) (Appellant) v Cheshire West and Chester Council and another (Respondents)*

*P and Q (by their litigation friend, the Official Solicitor) (Appellants) v Surrey County Council (Respondent) [2014] UKSC 19*

The Supreme Court looked at the cases of three people with learning disabilities who lacked capacity to be resident for care or treatment. Previously, lower courts had said they were having their liberty restricted but that they were not being deprived of their liberty. When the cases went to the Supreme Court, the seven judges there decided differently. The Supreme Court concluded that in fact, all three had been (and were continuing to be) deprived of their liberty as they were subject to *'complete supervision and control and not free to leave'.* This phrase is often referred to as the 'acid test'.

The three individuals, were known as P, MIG (or P) and MEG (or Q) to keep their real names anonymous. In this handbook, to avoid any confusion, they will be referred to as P, MIG and MEG. In explaining the judgment of the Supreme Court, Lady Hale stated:

*'Because of the extreme vulnerability of people like P, MIG and MEG, I believe that we should err on the side of caution in deciding what constitutes a deprivation of liberty in their case. They need a periodic independent check on whether the arrangements made for them are in their best interests.'*

Looking at the cases in order of the level of restrictions in place (most restricted first) the circumstances of each person, as summarised by the Supreme Court were as follows:

---

### **P's case**

P was aged 38 at the time of the first Court of Protection hearing. He was born with cerebral palsy and Down's syndrome and required 24 hour care to meet his personal care needs. Until he was 37 he lived with his mother, who was his principal carer, but her health began to deteriorate and the local social services authority concluded that she was no longer able to look after him. In 2009 they obtained orders from the Court of Protection that it was in P's best interests to live in accommodation arranged by the local authority. In his case, the court stated that: *'He could walk short distances but needed a wheelchair to go further. He also required prompting and help with all the activities of daily living, getting about, eating, personal hygiene and continence.'*

The more detailed circumstances of his care plan and life were as follows:

- P lived in a spacious bungalow close to his family home. He shared it with two other residents.
- P went to a day centre four days a week and to hydrotherapy once a week.
- He saw his mother regularly and had a good social life with visits to a club, pub and the shops.
- 98 hours additional one-to-one support were provided each week to help him leave the house whenever he wished.
- He had not tried to leave and the doors to the unit were only locked at night, but he was only allowed out if he was escorted.
- He was not on any medication to manage his behaviour.
- He was dressed in a body suit to prevent him eating his soiled continence pads (this was considered less restrictive than staff constantly restraining him to prevent him tearing pads).
- Physical restraint was required periodically (due to self-harm and aggression towards others).
- Two staff were on duty during the day with one member of staff awake overnight.

**MEG's case**

MEG (also referred to as Q in the court cases) had a learning disability but at the upper end of the moderate range, bordering on mild. She became the subject of care proceedings under the Children Act 1989 in 2007 when she was 15. Her communication skills were better than her sister's (see below) and her emotional understanding was quite sophisticated. She was also thought to have autistic traits and she exhibited challenging behaviour.

The details of her care plan and life were as follows:

- She lived in a small group home of four people with 24 hour staffing.
- No relatives actively opposed the placement.
- There were no restrictions on visitors and she had a good social life and went to college.
- It was not a locked environment and she had shown no wish to go out alone but had she tried to leave she would have been prevented from doing so.
- She had 1:1 and sometimes 2:1 support.
- She was restrained from 'time to time' when she exhibited challenging behaviour.
- Behavioural management techniques were being used and they were having a positive effect.
- She was being prescribed Risperidone (an antipsychotic) for the purpose of controlling her anxiety.

---

**MIG's case**

MIG (also referred to as P in the court cases) is the sister of MEG (above). She became the subject of care proceedings under the Children Act 1989 in 2007 when she was 16. She was 18 years old at the time of the first hearing with a severe learning disability (at the lower end of the moderate range or the upper end of the severe range). She also had problems with her sight, speech and hearing. The court described her as '*... incapable of independent living. She is largely dependent on others. She needs to be looked after save for basic care needs.'*

The detailed aspects of her care plan and life were as follows:

- She lived with her foster mother whom she called 'Mummy' and who is described as providing *intensive support* for MIG with most aspects of daily living.
- She had not tried to leave her placement and no relatives actively opposed it.
- The doors were not locked '*She has never sought to leave the home. If she were to try to leave she would be restrained for her own immediate safety.'*
- She was escorted outside because she was not safe to cross the road alone.
- She communicated with difficulty and had limited understanding, spending much of her time listening to music on her iPod.
- She was not in receipt of any medication and physical restraint was not used.
- There were no restrictions on visitors and she had a good social life and went to college.

---

**Progression through the courts**

The cases of P, MIG and MEG progressed to the Supreme Court because various parties at different stages did not agree with the rulings of the lower courts and wished to appeal the judges' decisions.

**Court of Protection (first stage)**
At this stage, the circumstances of MIG and MEG's case were decided NOT to be a deprivation of liberty. However, in P's case it WAS judged to be a deprivation of liberty.

**Court of Appeal (second stage)**
At this stage, all three cases were decided NOT to be a deprivation of liberty.

**The Supreme Court (third and final stage)**

The Supreme Court found that the circumstances of all three individuals meant that they were deprived of their liberty. Although they were receiving good care, not wanting or trying to leave, going out regularly and the families involved were not unhappy with the care, the circumstances of their care meant that they were subject to *'complete supervision and control and not free to leave'* and therefore deprived of their liberty.

The Court said that the concept of 'liberty' was the same for all people irrespective of whether they had a disability or any other condition. Lady Justice Hale, Deputy President of the Supreme Court, put it in the following way:

*'If it would be a deprivation of my liberty to be obliged to live in a particular place, subject to constant monitoring and control, only allowed out with close supervision, and unable to move away without permission even if such an opportunity became available, then it must also be a deprivation of the liberty of a disabled person.'*

Based on Lady Hale's assertion it would be prudent for staff who provide care for others to put themselves into the shoes of the people they care for (ignoring the fact they have no care needs themselves) and consider whether they would feel deprived of their liberty if placed in a care home, hospital or other care setting and subject to the same controls and restrictions.

A number of people have found the Supreme Court's judgment difficult to digest or apply because what had previously been referred to simply as care, can now also be referred to as a deprivation of liberty. The Supreme Court envisaged these concerns and stated:

*'Several objections may be raised to the conclusion that both MIG and MEG are being deprived of their liberty. One is that neither could survive without this level of supervision and control: but that is to resurrect the comparison with other people sharing their disabilities and to deny them the same concept of liberty as everyone else'.* It also noted: *'The Strasbourg court accepts that there are some people who are not capable of expressing a view either way and this is probably the case with both MIG and MEG. As HL 40 EHRR 761 shows, compliance is not enough.'*

Lord Neuberger, President of the Supreme Court, referring to previous European case law stated:

*'...the fact that 'the object is to protect treat or care in some way for the person taken into confinement' has 'no bearing on the question whether that person has been deprived of his liberty..."*

Lady Hale, Deputy President of the Supreme Court commented:

*'The fact that my living arrangements are comfortable, and indeed make my life as enjoyable as it could possibly be, should make no difference. A gilded cage is still a cage.'*

---

**What does *'complete supervision and control and not free to leave'* mean?**

This phrase, often referred to as the *acid test*, has two elements both of which must be met for a person to be assessed as being deprived of their liberty.

---

**1. Complete supervision and control**

The Supreme Court judgment moves between the terms 'continuous', 'complete' and 'constant' supervision and control however it does not appear to make a difference to the application of the test. The word 'continuous' appears in earlier European cases and is echoed in the Supreme Court Judgment. However, in the key passage where Lady Justice Hale sets out the acid test (paragraph 54), the word 'complete' is used:

*'If the acid test is whether a person is under the complete supervision and control of those caring for her and is not free to leave the place where she lives, then the truth is that both MIG and MEG are being deprived of their liberty.'*

In each of the three cases before the Supreme Court, the individuals had a 24 hour package of care and support (which enabled them to have fulfilling social lives) but the care plan was decided by others. Ultimately, the level of control over an individual is established by asking what would happen if they did not comply with elements of their care plan or the package of support.

The Supreme Court did not set out an exhaustive list of factors that explain what it means to be subject to complete supervision and control but it does appear from the cases they referred to (see below) that the following do **not** prevent a person from being described as deprived of their liberty:

- The person has overnight leave away from the hospital or care home.
- The person spends time (several hours or days) unobserved by staff.
- The person goes on periods of unescorted leave.
- The person goes on unescorted leave beyond the local area.

Unescorted leave

The three adults in the Supreme Court Cheshire West ruling were all escorted when outside and found to be deprived of their liberty. A person can however have unescorted leave and still be considered to be under 'complete supervision and control and not free to leave' and so deprived of their liberty. The ECHR has found this a number of times in cases such as:

- *Stanev v Bulgaria [2012] ECHR 46*
- *Ashingdane v UK [1985] ECHR 8*
- *Stankov v Bulgaria [2015] ECHR No. 25820/07*

In all of the cases above the people concerned had periods of unescorted leave but were still found to be deprived of their liberty because the leave was controlled and limited. It was the staff in their placements that decided if they could go out, when, for how long and would bring them back if they did not return. In a recent Welsh case concerning deprivation of liberty *(PJ v A local health board [2015] UKUT 0480 (AAC))* Mr Justice Charles stated:

*'...the fact that a person may have unescorted leave in the community does not mean that he is not deprived of his liberty if the leave is regulated and controlled, and he is not free to leave in the sense of removing himself permanently in order to live where and with whom he chooses.'*

---

## 2. Not free to leave

In all of the cases decided by the Supreme Court the people were going out regularly (escorted) but they were considered 'not free to leave' by the court. Free to leave refers to whether the person is free to remove themselves permanently from the placement. This is regardless of whether there is anywhere else for the individual to live. Whether they have shown any wish to live anywhere else is also irrelevant. The question for staff is: 'Would you stop the person from leaving if they ever tried to?' Note this is not an appropriate question to ask in Intensive Care Units or hospices, see page 119.

The Supreme Court referred to the case of *JE v DE and Surrey County Council [2006] EWHC 3459* in order to describe what it is to be free to leave. In this case, Surrey County Council tried to argue that a man in a care home was not deprived of his liberty because they were prepared to allow him to leave and live with his daughter or move to a different care home. They also highlighted that the man went on a number of trips and outings with his wife. However, Surrey County Council did not want to allow him to return to live with his wife and that was what he really wanted to do. In response to their arguments, the judge stated that for the purposes of the European Convention on Human Rights, freedom to leave was greater than Surrey County Council's proposal.

*'...I do not mean leaving for the purpose of some trip or outing approved by SCC or by those managing the institution: I mean leaving in the sense of removing himself permanently in order to live where and with whom he chooses ...'*

Freedom, according to the courts, means if you want to leave where you live, this should not be made conditional by the state. The majority of the population is free to live wherever they choose and to move whenever they want. Admittedly this may be limited by financial or family circumstances but the state does not impose direct limits on these choices.

In a recent case, *PJ v A Local Health Board and Others [2015] UKUT 480 (AAC)* a senior judge stated that the first part of the test should not be 'divorced' from the second:

*'It is expressed by Baroness Hale as a composite test with two parts. She envisages that a person who is not free to leave may not be not under <u>such</u> (my emphasis) continuous supervision and control as to found a conclusion that he or she is deprived of his or her liberty. But, she does not divide up the two parts in the way that the MHRT did by considering the degree of supervision and control in isolation and then not going on: i) to consider it with, or ii) to consider at all*

*whether PJ was free to leave (or effectively alter the conditions that limited his freedom action). Neither of the other majority judgments provide support for the approach taken by the MHRT.....in taking this approach to the key issue as identified by Baroness Hale, the MHRT overlooked that the fact that a person may have unescorted leave in the community does not mean that he is not deprived of his liberty if the leave is regulated and controlled, and he is not free to leave in the sense of removing himself permanently in order to live where and with whom he chooses.'*

---

### *Deprivation of liberty even if ...*

The Supreme Court ruling means that a person can be deprived of their liberty even though:

- **They are living in their own home** – a deprivation of liberty can happen anywhere if the circumstances meet the acid test. Lord Neuberger in the Supreme Court ruling[5] stated: *'...I cannot see any good reason why the fact that a person is confined to a domestic home, as opposed to a hospital or other institution, should prevent her from contending that she has been deprived of her liberty.'* A Court of Protection order is required to authorise this.

- **They are compliant or content or not objecting** – a person can be deprived of their liberty even though they are compliant and not objecting to the restrictions placed on them. Lord Neuberger in the Supreme Court ruling[5] stated: *'Her or his contentment with the conditions in which she finds herself does not determine whether she is restricted in her liberty. Liberty means the state or condition of being free from external constraint.'*

- **Family are not objecting** – a person's family or carers may consider the person's care to be right for them however the restrictions mean that they are being deprived of their liberty.

- **They lead a 'normal life'** – for some people certain restrictions might be required regardless of whether they live in a care home or family home. For example, they may need an escort when going out for reasons of safety. This may be true for all people with the same condition or disability. However, this does not affect the question of whether the restrictions in their care plan mean they are deprived of their liberty.

- **The purpose or aim of restrictions** – is beneficial and meets the person's care needs and keeps them safe. Lord Neuberger in the Supreme Court ruling noted: *'... the fact that 'the object is to protect treat or care in some way for the person taken into confinement' has 'no bearing on the question whether that person has been deprived of his liberty, although it might be relevant to the subsequent inquiry whether the deprivation of liberty was justified..." '*

- **The doors are NOT locked and the person goes out regularly** – even if the doors are not locked and a person is going out regularly (escorted or unescorted) they can still be found to be deprived of their liberty if they are subject to complete supervision and control and not free to leave. This relates to whether leave is controlled by the care provider and what staff would do if the person attempted to leave.

- **The placement is in their best interests** – even if a placement is meeting a person's needs, is in their best interests and there are no less restrictive options available, they can still be considered deprived of their liberty. Lady Hale stated: *'The facts of the two cases before us are a good illustration of the sort of benevolent living arrangements which many find difficult to characterise as a deprivation of liberty.'*

---

### Duties on local authorities

The responsibilities of local authorities to ensure staff understand DoLS was considered in the case of *G v E & Ors [2010] EWHC 3385 (Fam)*. The local authority tried to excuse its failure to recognise a deprivation of liberty due to a lack of understanding by staff. In response the judge stated: *'Miss Irving boldly relies on the ignorance of the local authority's staff as an excuse and submits that the complexity of the statutory provisions left large numbers of professionals uncertain as to the meaning of "deprivation of liberty". Given the enormous responsibilities put upon local authorities under the MCA, it was surely incumbent on the management team to ensure that their staff were fully trained and properly informed about the new provisions.'*

## Deprivation of Liberty: Case Study

The fictional case study below is designed to provide an idea of the potential restrictions in a care plan for someone in a care home (or equally in a hospital setting). An analysis of the restrictions is then given in relation to the Guzzardi factors (see page 15).

Simon is 74 years old and has Alzheimer's dementia. He lived at home alone for five years following his diagnosis with increasing levels of support provided by social services and his family. Over time the level of support available from social services could not meet his care needs and he was admitted to a care home with nursing support. The decision to move him was taken in his best interests under the Mental Capacity Act as he lacked the mental capacity to make the decision himself.

Simon is now settled in the care home and appears to enjoy the social environment and activities such as 'music time'. His family are pleased with the care he is receiving and visit him regularly. As a registered care home there are staff available 24 hours a day and residents' personal care is supported and dietary needs are met. Residents are encouraged to take part in an activity each morning or afternoon. The level of Simon's dementia means he presents a number of risks to himself and so in the kitchen he is not allowed to handle knives or make drinks with boiling water alone. Staff however provide appropriate support to enable him to make his own hot drinks as he enjoys this. He also needs support and supervision to ensure he washes and dresses appropriately each day and to ensure an appropriate level of hygiene is maintained.

Simon takes tablets for a long standing heart condition and the staff give these to him twice a day. The front door of the care home is locked but Simon is free to go out any time he wants as long as another adult is with him. He has never shown any wish to go out alone and he is supported to access the wider community on a regular basis with staff or his family escorting him. When asked Simon says he is very happy in the home and describes the places he visits and things he can do.

**Restrictions in Simon's care plan**

| Type | Duration | Manner | Effect | Degree/intensity |
|---|---|---|---|---|
| Decision about where to live made by others | All of the restrictions are ongoing and long term in nature. | This relates to how each restriction was 'imposed'. Questions would include how Simon's views and wishes were taken into account, whether his family were consulted, whether less restrictive options have been tried. | This relates to the effect of each restriction on Simon. If he had been moved many miles away from his family the effect of the restriction could have been that he saw significantly less of his family than before. | The degree or intensity of each restriction needs to be assessed. For example in terms of access to the kitchen; how often does he want to go into the kitchen versus how often staff are available, how long can he can stay in the kitchen and is he distressed by having to leave the kitchen or having access to it limited. |
| Monitoring – staff present 24 hours | | | | |
| Routine – a structured day | | | | |
| Access to kitchen restricted | | | | |
| Personal care supported and managed | | | | |
| Medication – held by staff | | | | |
| Doors locked and Simon cannot open them independently | | | | |
| Escorted outside | | | | |

Having identified and analysed the restrictions in the care plan a judgement has to be made about whether all the restrictions taken together mean Simon is subject to *'complete supervision and control and is not free to leave'.* The Supreme Court's threshold for this term was given in *Cheshire West*. Based on this case, Simon most likely would be judged to be deprived of his liberty.

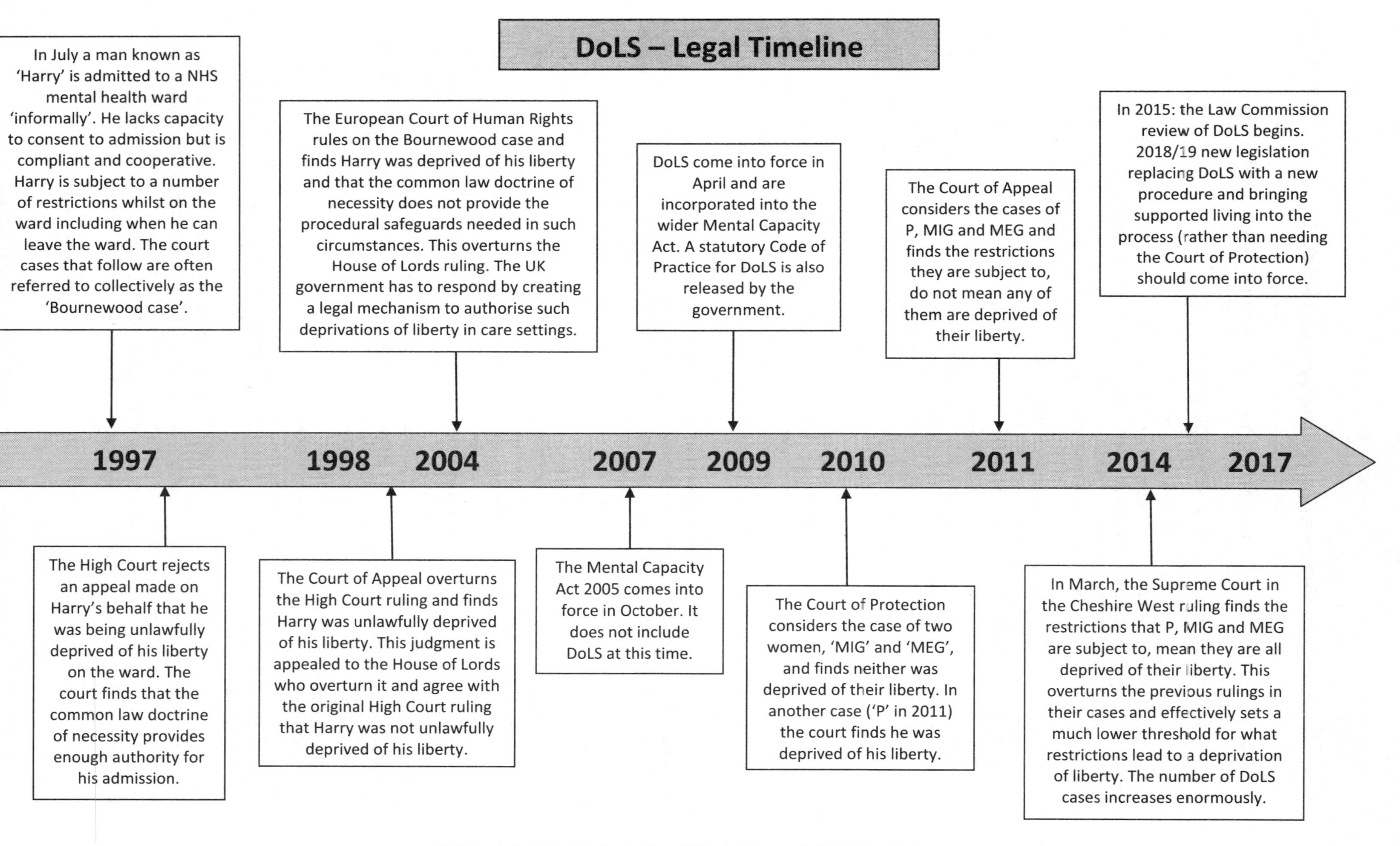
DoLS – Legal Timeline
In July a man known as 'Harry' is admitted to a NHS mental health ward 'informally'. He lacks capacity to consent to admission but is compliant and cooperative. Harry is subject to a number of restrictions whilst on the ward including when he can leave the ward. The court cases that follow are often referred to collectively as the 'Bournewood case'.
The High Court rejects an appeal made on Harry's behalf that he was being unlawfully deprived of his liberty on the ward. The court finds that the common law doctrine of necessity provides enough authority for his admission.
The Court of Appeal overturns the High Court ruling and finds Harry was unlawfully deprived of his liberty. This judgment is appealed to the House of Lords who overturn it and agree with the original High Court ruling that Harry was not unlawfully deprived of his liberty.
The European Court of Human Rights rules on the Bournewood case and finds Harry was deprived of his liberty and that the common law doctrine of necessity does not provide the procedural safeguards needed in such circumstances. This overturns the House of Lords ruling. The UK government has to respond by creating a legal mechanism to authorise such deprivations of liberty in care settings.
The Mental Capacity Act 2005 comes into force in October. It does not include DoLS at this time.
DoLS come into force in April and are incorporated into the wider Mental Capacity Act. A statutory Code of Practice for DoLS is also released by the government.
The Court of Protection considers the case of two women, 'MIG' and 'MEG', and finds neither was deprived of their liberty. In another case ('P' in 2011) the court finds he was deprived of his liberty.
The Court of Appeal considers the cases of P, MIG and MEG and finds the restrictions they are subject to, do not mean any of them are deprived of their liberty.
In March, the Supreme Court in the Cheshire West ruling finds the restrictions that P, MIG and MEG are subject to, mean they are all deprived of their liberty. This overturns the previous rulings in their cases and effectively sets a much lower threshold for what restrictions lead to a deprivation of liberty. The number of DoLS cases increases enormously.
In 2015: the Law Commission review of DoLS begins. 2018/19 new legislation replacing DoLS with a new procedure and bringing supported living into the process (rather than needing the Court of Protection) should come into force.
1997
1998
2004
2007
2009
2010
2011
2014
2017

## Frequently asked questions

- ***Specialist colleges*** – *Would an adult with a learning disability who lives at home with his parents but is taken by local authority transport to a specialist college each day be deprived of his liberty if the college lock the doors and do not let him out alone?*

The person's care should be looked at globally by the local authority that are funding the transport and college as this could be a deprivation of liberty especially as it is likely that when the man returns home he is also not allowed out alone. The person will need a court to consider whether a deprivation of liberty order should be given for the entire package of care including the time spent at the college. In the case of residential schools, it has been established that a deprivation of liberty can occur and would need authority from the Court of Protection. See cases of *R (C) v A Local Authority & Others [2011] EWHC 1539 (Admin)* and the more recent case of *Barnsley Metropolitan Borough Council v GS & Anor [2014] EWCOP 46* which confirmed the court's authority to make orders to deprive a person aged 18 or over of their liberty in a residential school. The situation for children and young people is considered in more detail at page 116.

---

- ***Respite care*** – *If a person is in a care home for respite for no more than 10 days would I need to apply for DoLS or is this just a restriction of their liberty?*

During this period of time if a person is subject to complete supervision and control and not free to leave, they would be deprived of their liberty. In these circumstances, a standard authorisation could be requested in advance of the respite taking place. If it is an urgent respite situation, an urgent authorisation would have to be applied by the care home. Law Society guidance[11] notes that a single standard authorisation could be used to authorise regular respite admissions during a period of time.

In the case of *AJ v A Local Authority [2015] EWCOP 5*, the Court of Protection warned against unlawful deprivations of liberty which start under the guise of short term respite when really the plan is to accommodate the person longer term. The judge said at paragraph 114: '... *professionals need to be on their guard to look out for cases where vulnerable people are admitted to residential care ostensibly for respite when the underlying plan is for a permanent placement without proper consideration as to their Article 5 rights.'*

---

- ***Physically bedridden*** – *If a person with a brain injury is physically bedridden, would this still mean they are deprived of their liberty?*

The cases before the Supreme Court remind us to ignore the fact that a person has a disability or a particular condition when answering the question as to whether someone is deprived of their liberty. For those that are physically bedridden the acid test remains the same. Accordingly, they could be deprived of their liberty if they are subject to complete supervision and control and not free to leave. However in relation to people in ICU and hospices please see page 119.

---

- ***Accident and emergency*** – *Can a person be deprived of their liberty in A&E?*

Yes. A person with a mental disorder in accident and emergency who lacks the mental capacity to consent to being there and is subject to complete supervision and control and not free to leave could be deprived of their liberty. The duration and intensity of the restrictions would be an important consideration in this situation. An example could be where a person is brought to A&E by police officers (not using powers of the Mental Health Act 1983) and they resist and try to leave (needing assessment and treatment but lacking capacity) and hospital staff ask the police to remain and prevent the person leaving. Further guidance is also available in the Law Society guide to identifying deprivation of liberty[11].

---

- ***Advance decisions*** – *Can a person write an advance decision when they have capacity stating they give their consent to future deprivations of liberty so DoLS is not required?*

No, an advance decision is only about the refusal of treatment so the above statement would not meet the criteria for an advance decision and therefore would not be legally binding. However, a person could make a statement to this effect and it would be taken into consideration as part of the DoLS assessment.

---

- ***Location*** – *If a person is not in a care home or hospital does DoLS apply?*

No, the safeguards do not apply. However there could still be a deprivation of liberty (DoL) which needs to be authorised. If a person is not in a care home or hospital and they are deprived of their liberty, an application to the Court of Protection must be made to authorise it (see page 121).

---

- ***Duration*** – *How long is it before restrictions or restraint become a deprivation of liberty?*

This is not a question that has been answered by the courts or the Act itself. There have been cases where very short periods of time have been acknowledged to be a deprivation of liberty due to the intensive restrictions applied to an individual. In one example, this was as short as 40 minutes due to the intensity of the restrictions where police officers used physical restraint, hand and leg cuffs and the caged area of a police vehicle in relation to a man with a learning disability *(ZH v Commissioner of Police for the Metropolis [2013] EWCA Civ 69)*. Although the most recent guidance by the Law Society[11] does not state an exact period (as it would be impossible to do), it suggests a deprivation will most likely begin following 2-3 days of restrictions. It could be sooner if there are particularly intense restrictions.

---

- ***DoLS for everyone*** – *Will everyone who lacks capacity in a care home or hospital need a DoLS authorisation?*

No. Even if a person lacks capacity to decide where to live, depending on the circumstances in which they are a resident or a patient, it may be the case that they are not being deprived of their liberty. The Law Society guidance[11] on deprivation of liberty however considers that for people who lack capacity to being admitted to care homes *with nursing care* it would be very unlikely that such admissions would not give rise to a deprivation of their liberty.

---

- ***Private care homes*** – *Does DoLS apply to private care homes?*

Yes. Any registered care home is covered by the legislation.

---

- ***Paying for DoLS*** – *Who pays for DoLS authorisations?*

The assessment process for authorisations is paid for by the local authority with money originating from central government. An authorisation does not place any responsibility on the clinical commissioning group, Welsh health board or local authority to pay for care.

---

- ***Privately arranged placements*** – *Are private residents, who have arranged their own placement and are paying for their own care, covered by DoLS?*

This is a complex area of law but the most recent guidance from the Law Society[11] indicates that even purely private arrangements in a private care home or hospital come within the DoLS procedure because these institutions are regulated by the state (the Care Quality Commission) therefore deprivation of liberty becomes imputable to the state.

## Urgent DoLS Authorisations

| | |
|---|---|
| **Summary** | The authority to deprive a person of their liberty in a care home or hospital if the person lacks the mental capacity to consent to be in the care home or hospital for care and/or treatment. It is used as a short term holding power whilst arrangements are made for a standard DoLS authorisation. An urgent authorisation is issued by the staff of a care home or hospital and is limited in duration to seven days or, in exceptional circumstances and with permission of the local authority, a maximum of 14 days. It cannot be extended beyond this time period. |
| **Legal criteria** | The care home or hospital believe the criteria (see page 37) for a standard DoLS authorisation are met<br>**and**<br>the care home or hospital believe they cannot wait for a standard authorisation before the deprivation of liberty begins because the person's needs are so urgent<br>**or**<br>they have already applied for a standard authorisation but they cannot wait for the standard authorisation to be given before the deprivation of liberty begins because the person's needs are so urgent. |
| **Powers** | ▪ *Deprivation of liberty* – authority to deprive a person of their liberty for up to seven days in a care home or hospital. With the agreement of the local authority an urgent authorisation can be extended from seven to a maximum of 14 days in duration.<br>▪ *Treatment and care for physical or mental health needs* – the person can be given treatment or care if they consent or, if they lack the mental capacity to consent, by using the Mental Capacity Act. Staff would need to assess the person's mental capacity and if the person lacks the mental capacity to consent to the act of treatment or care, make a decision in the person's best interests.<br>▪ *Absconding* – if the person absconds, they can be returned to the care home or hospital, using restraint if necessary (see page 11). |
| **Procedure** | A member of staff from the care home or hospital completes DoLS Form 1. At the time of completing the urgent DoLS authorisation, the care home or hospital must simultaneously request a standard DoLS authorisation from the local authority on the same form. It may be that a standard authorisation had already been requested but whilst waiting for this to be completed the situation changed and the person needed to be deprived of their liberty urgently.<br>The DoLS Code of Practice advises that family, friends and carers should, as far as practical and possible, be consulted and their views taken into account before an urgent DoLS authorisation is given. |
| **Who is involved?** | A member of staff from the care home or hospital. In relation to hospitals, the legislation does not state which person has authority to issue an urgent DoLS. For care homes, it is the registered manager. The DoLS Code of Practice appears to indicate this could be delegated. Local policies can specify which staff are permitted to complete and authorise an urgent DoLS authorisation. However, the DoLS Code of Practice (para 6.13) states that the decision should '*... be taken at a senior level'* within the care home or hospital. It is at the discretion of the organisation to decide which senior staff members this could be. |
| **Time limits** | An urgent authorisation can only last seven days (or a maximum of 14 in exceptional circumstances). |
| **Leave of absence** | The care home or hospital can allow the person to leave the premises at its discretion (see page 86). |

| | |
|---|---|
| **Patient rights** | <u>Appeals</u><br>To the Court of Protection (see page 84).<br><br><u>Advocacy</u><br>The right to an independent mental capacity advocate (IMCA) (see page 79).<br><br><u>Care Quality Commission (CQC)</u><br>CQC guidance[16] states: *'We have a duty to monitor the use of the Deprivation of Liberty Safeguards in all hospitals and care homes in England, and check on their use when we inspect the places where they are used.'* (see page 123) |
| **Duties on staff** | Care homes and hospitals must:<br><br>1. Keep records of all urgent authorisations they make, the reasons for them and any extensions requested from the local authority.<br><br>2. As soon as practical after making an urgent authorisation, give a copy of the urgent DoLS authorisation to the person concerned and any IMCA (39A type) that has been appointed by the local authority. (The DoLS Code of Practice also states that family, friends and carers should be notified as far as possible and appropriate to enable to them to support the person concerned.)<br><br>3. Take all practicable steps to ensure the person understands their legal rights and provide this information both orally and in writing. Unfortunately there is no statutory rights leaflet for people under DoLS. A rights leaflet for people on a standard DoLS is provided on page 136 and this can be amended for those under urgent DoLS.<br><br>4. Inform the person concerned if they request an extension of the urgent DoLS authorisation. If an extension is agreed the care home or hospital must give a copy of the notice to the person concerned and an IMCA (if appointed).<br><br>5. Inform the CQC (standard form) whenever an urgent authorisation is completed.<br><br>The local authority also has a number of duties and responsibilities (see page 93). |
| **Ending an urgent authorisation** | While the application of an urgent authorisation sets the *maximum* period of its duration, it does not compel a care home or hospital to deprive a person of their liberty for the duration stated. For example, if there is no need for deprivation of liberty following the fifth day, restrictions should be lifted so the person is no longer under an urgent DoLS.<br><br>There are a number of ways for an urgent authorisation to end:<br><br>▪ By an order of the Court of Protection.<br><br>▪ Lapse of the urgent authorisation. Allowing an authorisation to expire through the passage of time would not be considered good practice as any deprivation of liberty should end as soon as the legal criteria no longer applies. In addition, an urgent authorisation should only be applied if the care home or hospital also intends to apply for a standard authorisation. Once an urgent authorisation expires, there is no further authority to detain unless the standard authorisation has been granted or the urgent authorisation has been extended.<br><br>▪ If either a standard authorisation is granted or the local authority refuses to grant one, the urgent authorisation ends immediately. The relevant time for the purpose of ending the urgent authorisation is when the care home or hospital receives notice from the local authority regarding whether the standard authorisation has been given.<br><br>▪ Not meeting one or more of the DoLS criteria. If a person for example regains mental capacity whilst under the authorisation it must end. The care home or hospital must then inform the local authority accordingly. |

**Extending an urgent DoLS authorisation**

An urgent authorisation allows deprivation of liberty for up to seven days. This may be extended by a further seven days if the care home or hospital requests this from the local authority (Form 1). The local authority must consider there to be '*exceptional circumstances*' for doing so. The extension can only take place once and the local authority will notify the care home or hospital of its decision.

The Act does not give a detailed definition of exceptional circumstances. The DoLS Code of Practice (para 4.11) states: *'It is for the supervisory body to decide what constitutes an 'exceptional reason', but because of the seriousness of the issues involved, the supervisory body's decision must be soundly based and defensible. It would not, for example, be appropriate to use staffing shortages as a reason to extend an urgent authorisation.'*

An example given in the DoLS Code of Practice is that if a best interests assessor has not been able to speak with a key person and that person's input is essential to the assessment, then an extension may be permissible.

The CQC has noted[10] with concern a wide variation in practice between local authorities in extending urgent authorisations: *'We expect local authorities to keep this under review and to make sure that any extensions to the deadlines are kept to a minimum. We will explore the variations in practice among local authorities in the future.'*

Following the Supreme Court ruling in *Cheshire West* many urgent authorisations have been extended because local authorities did not have enough trained assessors to meet the huge increase in DoLS applications.

**Forms**

The application is made using DoLS Form 1. Please note that the forms are not statutory and some local authorities have amended them to suit local practice (see page 126). DoLS Form 1 is also used for requesting extensions of urgent DoLS beyond seven days.

**Guidance**

The DoLS Code of Practice (para 6.2) notes: *'Urgent authorisations should normally only be used in response to sudden unforeseen needs. However, they can also be used in care planning (for example, to avoid delays in transfer for rehabilitation, where delay would reduce the likely benefit of the rehabilitation).'* An example of this could be an urgent admission from a care home to a hospital where the person has to stay as an inpatient for some treatment. The hospital may need to use an urgent DoLS authorisation to give them permission to deprive the person of their liberty. They cannot rely on the standard DoLS authorisation from the care home as it cannot be transferred.

In the case of *AJ v A Local Authority [2015] EWCOP 5 the* Court of Protection stated:

*'... I emphasise that the scheme of the DoLS is that, in the vast majority of cases, it should be possible to plan in advance so that a standard authorisation can be obtained before the deprivation of liberty begins. It is only in exceptional cases, where the need for the deprivation of liberty is so urgent that it is in the best interests of the person for it to begin while the application is being considered, that a standard authorisation need not be sought before the deprivation begins.'*

## Standard DoLS Authorisations

**Summary**

The authority to deprive a person of their liberty in a care home or hospital if the person lacks the mental capacity to consent to be in the care home or hospital for care and/or treatment. A standard authorisation lasts for up to one year at a time. It is authorised externally by a local authority following assessments undertaken by a minimum of two independent assessors.

**Legal criteria**

The person is at least *18 years* old (age assessment – see page 39)
+
The person has a *mental disorder* (mental health assessment – see page 38)
+
the person *lacks mental capacity* to decide whether to be in a care home or hospital for the purpose of receiving care/treatment
(mental capacity assessment – see page 47)
+
there are *no refusals* (no refusals assessment – see page 40)
+
the person is *eligible* for DoLS (eligibility assessment – see page 66)
+
the person is, or is going to be, deprived of their liberty and it is in the person's *best interests* to be deprived of their liberty in the care home or hospital and it is necessary to prevent harm to them and the deprivation of liberty is a proportionate response to the likelihood and the seriousness of that harm occurring (best interests assessment – see page 56).

**Powers**

- *Deprivation of liberty* – the authority to deprive a person of their liberty for up to 12 months in a care home or hospital.
- *Treatment and care for physical or mental health needs* – the person can be given treatment or care if they consent or, if they lack the mental capacity to consent, by using the Mental Capacity Act. Staff would need to assess the person's mental capacity (Sections 1-3 of the Act) and if the person lacks the mental capacity to consent to the act of treatment or care, make a decision in the person's best interests (Sections 1 and 4 of the Act).
- *Absconding* – if the person absconds, they can be returned to the care home or hospital, using restraint if necessary (see page 11).

---

**Procedure**

A care home or hospital is required to request a standard DoLS assessment when:

1. A person is due to be placed with them and they believe the person will be deprived of their liberty on admission or within 28 days of it.
2. They have an existing resident who is likely to be deprived of their liberty in the next 28 days.
3. They have an existing resident who is already being deprived of their liberty.
4. A standard DoLS authorisation is already in place but the resident is going to move to a new care home or hospital. The new care home or hospital will need to request a DoLS authorisation.

Note: Please see guidance on page 93 for local authorities regarding their duties.

The care home or hospital must apply in writing to their local authority using DoLS Form 1 (see page 126) and provide the information requested on the form.

Relatives, friends, carers or anyone else involved can also request a DoLS assessment (see page 90 for further details).

| | |
|---|---|
| **Who is involved?** | A minimum of two professional and independent assessors are required, a doctor (called a mental health assessor) and a health or social care professional (not a doctor) called a best interests assessor (BIA). They undertake different assessments but, between them, their assessments must confirm that all the criteria for a standard authorisation are met. |
| **Time limits** | The assessments must be completed by the local authority within 21 days (including weekends and public holidays) of the local authority receiving the request. However, if an urgent authorisation is already in force, the assessments must be completed by the end of the urgent authorisation (which will usually be a maximum of seven days but could be up to 14 days in exceptional circumstances).<br><br>Please note that due to the huge increase in applications following the Supreme Court ruling in *Cheshire West*, this timescale has not always been adhered to. |
| **Leave of absence** | The care home or hospital can allow the person to have periods of leave at its discretion (see page 86). |
| **Patient rights** | Appeal<br>The right of appeal to the Court of Protection at any point whilst under a standard authorisation (see page 84).<br><br>Review<br>The right to a review at any time (see page 82).<br><br>Advocacy<br>The right to an independent mental capacity advocate (IMCA) (see page 79).<br><br>Representative<br>The right to independent support from a representative (see page 75).<br><br>Care Quality Commission<br>CQC guidance[16] states: *'We have a duty to monitor the use of the Deprivation of Liberty Safeguards in all hospitals and care homes in England, and check on their use when we inspect the places where they are used.'* (see page 123)<br><br>Assessments<br>The local authority is responsible for ensuring a copy of the assessments authorising the deprivation of liberty is given to the person under DoLS and their representative. |
| **Duties on staff** | There is a legal duty on care homes and hospitals to take all practicable steps to ensure the person under DoLS understands their legal rights and they must provide this information both orally and in writing in a way the person is most able to understand.<br><br>Information on legal rights includes the effect of the authorisation, the right to appeal, the right to a review and the right to an IMCA. There is no statutory rights leaflet for people under DoLS. A booklet called 'DoLS and You' is available from the Department of Health although it is not a formal rights leaflet. An example of a rights leaflet for use by care home or hospital staff is given on page 136.<br><br>Staff must inform the CQC whenever a standard authorisation is requested or completed for a person. This includes whenever the authorisation is extended for another period of time. The CQC has a standard online form for this purpose.<br><br>Staff should also record and monitor how often a representative is in contact with the person and inform the local authority (see page 75).<br><br>Local authorities must keep a written record of every request they receive and the outcome, regardless of whether an authorisation is granted at the end of the assessment process.<br><br>Further information on duties for care homes, hospitals and local authorities is given on pages 93 and 97. |

**Ending the DoLS authorisation**

There are a number of ways for a standard DoLS authorisation to end:

- The Court of Protection – following an appeal or other application (see page 84).
- Following a review (see page 82).
- Lapse of the authorisation at the end of the period granted. Allowing an authorisation to expire through the passage of time would not be considered good practice as any deprivation of liberty should end as soon as the legal criteria no longer applies to the person concerned.
- The care home or hospital can lift the restrictions on a person and discharge them but the local authority must be notified so it can officially end the DoLS authorisation (DoLS Form 9).
- Not meeting one or more of the criteria. If a person, for example, regains capacity to be resident for care whilst under a DoLS, this will end the DoLS as the legal criteria are no longer met. A review should take place immediately to confirm this and allow the local authority to end the DoLS authorisation formally.

---

**Further standard authorisation**

If another period of authorisation is necessary, a new application should be made using DoLS Form 2. There is no time limit on how early this application may be made but if it is too early, the person's circumstances may change.

---

**Forms**

DoLS Form 1 is used to make the application. Form 9 is used to end it and Form 2 to request a further authorisation. DoLS Forms 3 and 4 are completed by the DoLS assessors appointed by the local authority and Form 5 formally grants and begins a standard DoLS authorisation on behalf of the local authority.

---

**Guidance**

The DoLS Code of Practice (para 3) states: *'In the vast majority of cases, it should be possible to plan in advance so that a standard authorisation can be obtained before the deprivation of liberty begins'.*

---

**Questions**

*Can a standard authorisation be granted to come into force at some time in the future?*

Yes. Paragraph 63(2) of Schedule A1 (DoLS) allows for this. A judge in the case of *KD v A Borough Council, the Department of Health and Others [2015] UKUT 251 (AAC)* also confirmed that this was the case with Court of Protection orders when he said: *'...in my view the Court of Protection can approve a care plan and authorise any deprivation of liberty it would create from a date in the future (i.e. when it comes into effect).'*

*When a standard DoLS is requested does this provide the authority to deprive the person of their liberty whilst they are being assessed?*

No. The 21 day assessment period for a standard authorisation does not include the authority to deprive the person of their liberty. It is only once the authorisation is granted by the local authority at the end of the assessment process that deprivation of liberty is authorised. The Code of Practice advises that the authorisation should be obtained in advance whenever possible. If this is not possible, an urgent authorisation should be used. In the case of *AJ v A Local Authority [2015] EWCOP 5*, the judge stated:

*'... in the vast majority of cases, it should be possible to plan in advance so that a standard authorisation can be obtained before the deprivation of liberty begins. It is only in exceptional cases, where the need for the deprivation of liberty is so urgent that it is in the best interests of the person for it to begin while the application is being considered, that a standard authorisation need not be sought before the deprivation begins.'*

## Admission to care homes and other residential placements

(places **not** registered to use the Mental Health Act 1983)

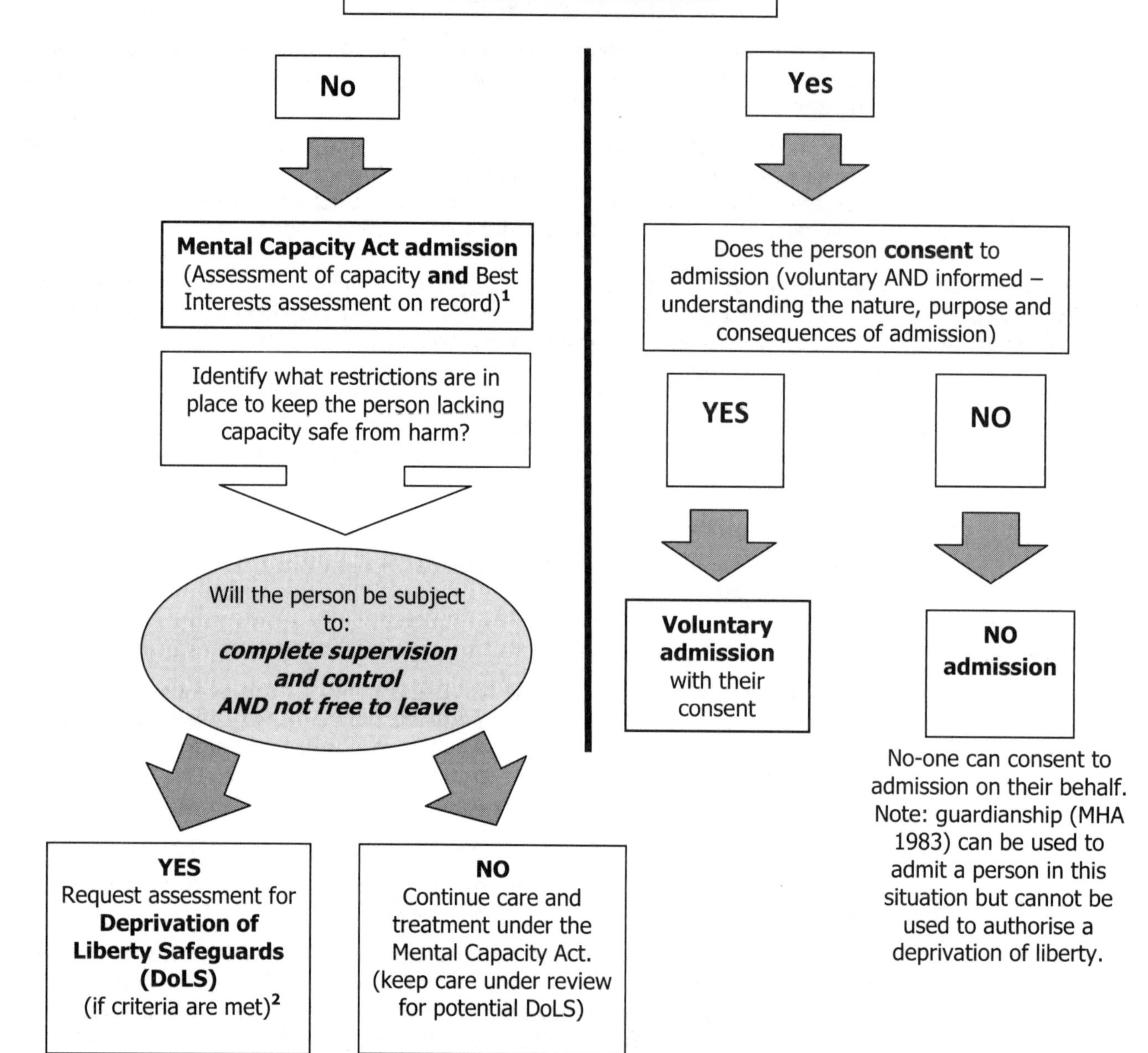


**1.** If a person has a personal welfare Lasting Power of Attorney (or deputy) then the attorney decides/authorises admission and care. An attorney nor deputy cannot however authorise a deprivation of liberty.

**2.** People aged 16-17 or people not living in a care home or hospital require an order from the Court of Protection (refer to your local authority DoLS office for guidance).

## Standard DoLS Authorisations – The Assessments (Legal Criteria)

To complete a standard DoLS authorisation, a person must meet certain statutory criteria. A series of six assessments undertaken by the mental health assessor and the best interests assessor appointed by the local authority confirm whether the person meets these criteria. For urgent DoLS authorisations, the care home or hospital must confirm they believe all the assessments are met. The assessments can be undertaken in any order and several are completed by each assessor so, for example a best interests assessor could complete four of the assessments in a single visit.

The assessments, which must be met for either an urgent or standard DoLS authorisation, are summarised below with full details given on the following pages. In addition, guidance on the completion of the DoLS forms by assessors is also given on page 127.

**1. Mental health**

- The person has a mental disorder (page 38).

**2. Age**

- They are aged 18 or over (page 39).

**3. No refusals**

- There is no advance decision, lasting power of attorney or deputy opposing the proposed DoLS (page 40).

**4. Mental capacity**

- The person lacks the mental capacity to decide whether to be accommodated in the care home or hospital for care or treatment (page 47).

**5. Best interests**

- The person is (or will be) deprived of their liberty in the care home or hospital AND it is in their best interests AND it is necessary to prevent harm to them AND it is a proportionate response (page 56).

**6. Eligibility**

- The person is not or should not be detained under the Mental Health Act 1983 and is therefore eligible for DoLS (page 66).

## Mental Health Assessment

If a person is to be deprived of their liberty because of their mental disorder, the law requires objective medical evidence of the mental disorder to be provided. Accordingly, in order for a DoLS authorisation to be granted, a mental health assessment is required. The legal definition of a mental disorder used for DoLS is the same as that used by the Mental Health Act 1983 (Section 1) which is:

*'...any disorder or disability of the mind'*

The Mental Health Act Code of Practice (para 2.5) gives the following conditions that could be classed as mental disorders within this definition:

*'• affective disorders, such as depression and bipolar disorder*
*• schizophrenia and delusional disorders*
*• neurotic, stress-related and somatoform disorders, such as anxiety, phobic disorders, obsessive compulsive disorders, post-traumatic stress disorder and hypochondriacal disorders*
*• organic mental disorders such as dementia and delirium (however caused)*
*• personality and behavioural changes caused by brain injury or damage (however acquired)*
*• personality disorders*
*• mental and behavioural disorders caused by psychoactive substance use*
*• eating disorders, non-organic sleep disorders and non-organic sexual disorders*
*• learning disabilities*
*• autistic spectrum disorders (including Asperger's syndrome)*
*• behavioural and emotional disorders of children and young people*

*(Note: this list is not exhaustive.)'*

Dependence on alcohol or drugs is not a mental disorder in relation to DoLS or the Mental Health Act and therefore a person cannot be deprived of their liberty under either law for this reason alone. However, a person who has schizophrenia and a dependence on alcohol, for example, would meet the criteria of having a mental disorder due to their schizophrenia.

---

**Learning disability**

DoLS differs to the Mental Health Act in its application for people with a learning disability. If a person has a learning disability it does *not* need to be associated with *'abnormally aggressive or seriously irresponsible conduct'* for DoLS to be used. This requirement is contained in the Mental Health Act 1983 and excludes those with a learning disability from being detained under some sections of the Mental Health Act *unless* the learning disability is associated with such conduct. However, *anyone* with a learning disability would meet the criteria of having a mental disorder for the purposes of an authorisation under DoLS. They would, of course, also have to meet all the other DoLS criteria before their deprivation of liberty could be authorised.

---

**DoLS and the wider Mental Capacity Act**

The Mental Capacity Act first came into force without DoLS in October 2007. To use the wider Act to deliver care and treatment generally, a person needs to lack capacity because of '... *an impairment of, or a disturbance in the functioning of, the mind or brain'* (Section 2 of the Act). This is a much wider 'gateway' disorder than that for DoLS. For example, a person with a urinary tract infection or someone who is drunk in A&E and lacks mental capacity to consent to treatment as a result would meet the requirements of the Mental Capacity Act and treatment could be given in their best interests. However, they could not be assessed under DoLS because they would not meet the criteria of having a mental disorder. Accordingly, DoLS applies to a narrower group of people than the Mental Capacity Act as a whole.

**The assessment**

The mental health assessment can only be undertaken by a DoLS mental health assessor (a doctor) using DoLS Form 4. It requires the assessor to confirm they reasonably believe the person has a mental disorder meeting the definition of DoLS. This means the assessment should present the evidence for a mental disorder. The form asks for: *'a rationale for your opinion, including details of their symptoms, diagnosis and behaviour'.*

In addition to assessing whether the person has a mental disorder, the Act states the assessor must also: '... *consider how (if at all) the relevant person's mental health is likely to be affected by his being a detained resident, and ... notify the best interests assessor of his conclusions'.*

This assessment could include positive, negative and neutral statements. For example, a person who is being moved from their own home to a care home under DoLS may experience the loss of familiar surroundings and emotional distress because they are leaving their home. However, they may also benefit from an improvement in their mental health because they may have suffered anxiety at home as their ability to live independently deteriorated. It may be the case that for a person with advanced dementia, an assessor is not able to draw any conclusions about how DoLS would affect the person's mental health.

There is no requirement on the mental health assessor to state whether they believe the person requires treatment or is being deprived of their liberty.

## Age Assessment

There is a statutory requirement that a person must be at least 18 years old in order for DoLS to be used. The deprivation of liberty of young people aged 16 and 17 who lack capacity can be authorised by the Court of Protection or other legal authority (see page 116).

The DoLS Code of Practice (para 4.23) advises that if there is doubt about the person's age, this assessment can be completed by checking the person's birth certificate or *'... other evidence that the assessor considers reliable'.* If no evidence is available, the assessor must use their own judgment.

This assessment must be undertaken by a DoLS best interests assessor (see page 91) and is recorded on DoLS Form 3.

## No Refusals Assessment

The purpose of this assessment, as suggested by the title, is to establish whether there is any formal authority to refuse or oppose the use of DoLS being proposed. There are three possible sources of a refusal that can stop (or block) the use of DoLS under this assessment:

1. an advance decision
2. a lasting power of attorney
3. a deputy

It is important to note that an advance decision, lasting power of attorney and deputy *may* have the power to prevent a DoLS authorisation from being granted but they do NOT have the power to authorise it themselves. Only the Court of Protection has this additional power to deprive a person of their liberty.

The no refusals assessment can only be undertaken by a DoLS best interests assessor. It is completed using DoLS Form 3. Guidance for completion of Form 3 is given on page 127.

---

## 1. Advance decisions

The terms 'advance directive' and 'living will' are reasonably well known. The Mental Capacity Act uses the term 'advance decision' and provides a statutory procedure for making such decisions. An advance decision is a statement made by a person with mental capacity stating their wish to refuse future treatment. The statement only becomes effective if the person, at a later date, lacks the mental capacity to make a decision regarding the treatment in question. The Act asserts the legal authority of advance decisions and makes it clear that they must be followed when valid and applicable to the treatment proposed.

The Mental Capacity Act Code of Practice (para 98) states: '... *healthcare professionals should always start from the assumption that a person who has made an advance decision had capacity to make it, unless they are aware of reasonable grounds to doubt the person had the capacity to make the advance decision at the time they made it.'*

Advance decisions allow people to refuse treatment but not care. For example, a person could make a valid advance decision refusing blood transfusions or resuscitation but not to state their refusal to a care home admission. Such a refusal will still be taken into account if the person later lacks capacity as it will provide evidence of their past wishes in the case of a best interests decision. However, it would not be legally binding on those placing the person in a care home.

An advance decision is relevant to a DoLS authorisation if the reason for the admission is to deliver treatment which the person has already objected to in a valid and applicable advance decision. If there is no other reason that the person is being admitted, the DoLS criteria cannot be met and the authorisation cannot be granted.

---

In relation to advance decisions, best interests assessors need to:

1. ascertain whether a person has a valid advance decision
2. determine whether a valid advance decision relates to the reason for the proposed DoLS authorisation.

Best interests assessors may be asked to provide evidence of the steps or actions they took to confirm the existence of an advance decision and it would be wise to record this. Reasonable steps would include: a) asking the person directly b) asking the staff of the care home or hospital c) asking family or other involved people d) checking with the person's GP if a copy is lodged with them.

---

### Requirements

In order for an advance decision to be valid in law, the person making it must have had the capacity to make it and have been at least 18 years old at the time. The MCA Code of Practice states that the treatment being refused must be specified even if it is described in lay terms, for example 'do not put me on a machine that breathes for me'. It goes on to explain (para 9.11) that an advance decision: *'...must state precisely what treatment is to be refused – a statement giving a general desire not to be treated is not enough.'* Some people may however wish to refuse all medical intervention. The MCA Code of Practice (para 9.13) states: *'An advance decision refusing all treatment in any situation (for example, where a person explains that their decision is based on their religion or personal beliefs) may be valid and applicable'.*

---

### Verbal advance decisions

An advance decision can be made verbally as long as it does not apply to life-sustaining treatment. Although there is no set format, the MCA Code of Practice provides guidance to staff (para 9.23) on how to record this type of advance decision:

- *'A note that the decision should apply if the person lacks capacity to make treatment decisions in the future*
- *A clear note of the decision, the treatment to be refused and the circumstances in which the decision will apply*
- *Details of someone who was present when the oral advance decision was recorded and the role in which they were present (for example, healthcare professional or family member)*
- *Whether they heard the decision, took part in it or are just aware that it exists'*

---

### Written advance decisions

An advance decision to refuse life-sustaining treatment must meet the legal criteria below:

1. It is in writing (this can include being written in the healthcare notes and does not have to be physically written by the person themselves if, for example, they are physically unable to do so).

**and**

2. It is signed by the person or by someone else in their presence as directed by them.

**and**

3. The above signature is witnessed and the witness signs the advance decision. NOTE: If the author of the advance decision directed someone else to sign on their behalf, the witness must witness this direction and then also sign to confirm they have witnessed this.

**and**

4. The decision must include a statement making it clear that it applies to that particular treatment even if the person's life is at risk.

As there are no statutory forms for making advance decisions, they can be handwritten in any format providing they meet the criteria. The witness to an advance decision can be any person and there is no requirement under the Act to use a solicitor. An advance decision to refuse treatment could also include circumstances in which it would apply, for example, a refusal of any form of surgery if the person lacks capacity because of dementia.

---

- *Question: What if someone has a vested interest in the person making the advance decision and they help them complete it and also act as the witness?*

There are no legal requirements regarding the person that acts as a witness although the MCA Code of Practice states that it may be helpful to describe the relationship between the person making it and the witness. Any concerns about the validity of the witness' signature may be brought before the Court of Protection. The witness must be a different person to the person transcribing the advance decision. Therefore, if a person has asked someone else to write out the advance decision because they cannot physically do so themselves, three people will be involved in making the advance decision – the author (stating their wishes), the person transcribing and the witness.

- *Question: Can the witness be a nurse or doctor providing care to the person concerned?*

Yes. There is nothing in the legislation to prevent this. The MCA Code of Practice states (para 9.21): *'It is possible that a professional acting as a witness will also be the person who assesses the person's capacity. If so, the professional should also make a record of the assessment, because acting as a witness does not prove that there has been an assessment.'*

- *Question: Is life-sustaining treatment defined?*

Section 4(10) of the Act states it is *'... treatment which in the view of a person providing healthcare for the person concerned is necessary to sustain life'.* Artificial nutrition and hydration (ANH) is classed as medical treatment and therefore can be refused via an advance decision. ANH means feeding and hydration via nasogastric tube, PEG tube, subcutaneous means or intravenous methods.

---

**Cancelling or changing advance decisions**

A person can withdraw or alter an advance decision at any time provided they have the mental capacity to do so. A cancellation does not have to be in writing even if the advance decision was refusing life-sustaining treatment. The MCA Code of Practice advises staff to record any cancellation in the healthcare records. The person themselves should destroy any written advance decision as soon as possible once they have decided it no longer applies.

An alteration to an advance decision does not need to be in writing *unless* it now applies to life-sustaining treatment. For example, if the person initially made a verbal advance decision to refuse antibiotics and they now want the same decision to apply even if their life is at risk (that is, to refuse life-sustaining treatment) it must be in writing and follow the legal criteria detailed earlier.

---

**Record holding**

There is no formal place to hold an advance decision or any statutory forms to make one. The person making the advance decision should take steps to ensure staff that treat them are aware of its existence. The MCA Code of Practice (para 9.56) states: *'Healthcare professionals should not delay emergency treatment to look for an advance decision if there is no clear indication that one exists.'*

---

**Legal authority of advance decisions**

Those treating a person will not incur any liability for following an advance decision (and not giving the stated treatment) provided they reasonably believe the advance decision is valid and applicable to the treatment. However, staff that knowingly ignore a valid advance decision could face criminal (they could be prosecuted) or civil (they could be sued) legal action against them.

---

**Limitations**

Advance decisions can only legally *refuse* treatment. Although a person may make a statement requesting certain treatments (rather than refusing them), their request is not legally enforceable and will not necessarily be followed. Nevertheless, these statements or requests are valuable if a person loses capacity and treatment decisions are being made in their best interests. This is because the best interests checklist within Section 4 of the Act would be applied which includes the requirement to consider any wishes or statements the person had made before they lost capacity.

The MCA Code of Practice notes that an advance decision cannot be made to refuse care that is needed to keep a person comfortable (also known as basic or essential care) such as warmth, shelter and the offer of food or water by mouth.

---

**An advance decision is NOT valid if:**

- A lasting power of attorney was created after the advance decision, which gave the attorney authority to give or refuse consent to treatment, to which the advance decision relates. In this situation, the attorney takes precedence and their authority must be sought to proceed with treatment. However, the existence of any other form of lasting power of attorney will not invalidate the advance decision.

- The person has clearly acted in a way contrary to the advance decision.
- At the time of treatment the person has capacity to give or refuse consent.
- The treatment planned is not specified in the advance decision.
- Any circumstances specified in the advance decision are absent.
- There are reasonable grounds to believe that circumstances have changed to such an extent that they would have affected the original decision. For example, new medication that significantly changes the outlook for a particular condition may be available. It might be argued that if the person knew this information, they would not have refused that treatment.

If any of the situations above apply, the advance decision may become invalid and staff would not be obliged to follow it. In cases of dispute about whether an advance decision is valid and applicable, the MCA Code of Practice advises that the healthcare professional in charge of the person's care should consult with all relevant people such as their colleagues and the patient's family and friends. However, the healthcare professional in charge is responsible for making the final decision. In cases of uncertainty that cannot be resolved easily, an application should be made to the Court of Protection (see page 84). This may have to be on an emergency basis.

---

**Mental Health Act 1983**

Although a valid and applicable advance decision may prevent a DoLS authorisation from being granted, the Mental Health Act 1983 can be considered instead if the treatment is for the person's mental disorder (this would include physical treatment which is treating a symptom of the mental disorder such as treating wounds caused by self harm). Further legal advice may need to be sought if this is the case as the courts have respected an advance decision to refuse treatment even though the Mental Health Act 1983 was in force and could have overridden it. See the case of *Nottinghamshire Healthcare NHS Trust v RC [2014] EWHC 1317 (COP).*

---

## 2. Lasting Power of Attorney

A lasting power of attorney for personal welfare (health and social care) can be used to give someone else the authority to make decisions for another person if that person ever lacks the mental capacity to make them for themselves. The attorney can be anyone of that person's choice as long as they are at least 18 years old and have the mental capacity to act.

To avoid confusion, for the purposes of this section, the following terms will be used:

*Donor* – the person who has made the decision to appoint an attorney.

*Attorney* – the person appointed by the donor to make decisions on their behalf (attorneys are more formally known as 'donees' under the Act).

To appoint an attorney under the Act, the donor must be at least 18 years old and have capacity. The lasting power of attorney can be registered at any time but it cannot be used until it has been registered. The donor can register it whilst they have capacity, or it may be registered by the attorney at any time after the donor has lost capacity.

If the person to be deprived of their liberty has a personal welfare attorney and any part of the DoLS authorisation would be in conflict with a valid decision the attorney has made, the authorisation cannot be granted. It may be appropriate to remove a proposed condition to try and accommodate the attorney's objections in order that the authorisation can then proceed. In the event there is concern that an attorney is acting contrary to a donor's best interests, an application may be made to the Court of Protection to request the court removes the attorney's powers. If this is successful, a DoLS authorisation may then be used at a later date.

---

**DoLS best interests assessors checklist for attorneys**

In relation to lasting powers of attorney, best interests assessors, as part of their assessment, need to check the following:

1. Does the person have a lasting power of attorney?
2. Is it valid and registered? See below for details on how to check the register.
3. Do the powers in it cover the proposed DoLS authorisation? For example, the attorney may have the authority to decide where the person lives.
4. Does the attorney oppose the DoLS authorisation? It is important for the BIA to explain clearly to an attorney that they are being consulted because they can refuse a DoLS authorisation if they disagree with it. The BIA should directly ask the attorney if they oppose the proposed DoLS authorisation and record this on DoLS Form 3 otherwise an attorney could claim they were merely consulted about the DoLS without being told of their right to refuse it.

A best interests assessor may be asked what steps they took to confirm whether there was a lasting power of attorney. This could include: a) asking the person being assessed b) speaking with staff of the care home or hospital c) checking the records of the care home or hospital d) speaking with family or other interested people e) checking the register of the Public Guardian (where it appears points a-d are not reliable, for example the person lacks capacity and has no family or friends).

Each page of a registered lasting power of attorney form will show a stamp from the Office of the Public Guardian. The DoLS assessor should ask to see this evidence. If they are concerned about the validity of the attorney's evidence, or the attorney cannot produce it, the assessor can ask the Office of the Public Guardian to search the register of attorneys. This service is free, quick and done by completing Form OPG100.

The lasting power of attorney form does not include photographic identification, so the only way of confirming that the person is the attorney they claim to be, would be to match their name to some other photographic identification such as a driving licence.

Please also note that the standard lasting power of attorney forms have changed in appearance since the introduction of the Mental Capacity Act and they may look different and be of varying lengths. At the time of writing, the form is 11 pages but an older variant of the form (which could still be valid) was approximately 26 pages in length.

---

**Personal welfare (health and social care) decisions**

Where the donor authorises the attorney to make health and social care decisions, the following rules apply:

1. An attorney only has authority to make decisions if the person concerned lacks capacity to make those decisions themselves.
2. If the person lacks capacity but has an advance decision (covering the same decision(s) as the lasting power of attorney) and the advance decision was made after the attorney was appointed, the advance decision will override the authority of the attorney. On the other hand, if the advance decision was made before the lasting power of attorney, the attorney can decide to override the advance decision if it is in the best interests of the person.
3. The attorney can be given the power to give or refuse consent to life-sustaining treatment, however the lasting power of attorney form must clearly state this authority.
4. Where a person is detained under a section of the Mental Health Act 1983 to which the compulsory treatment powers of the Mental Health Act apply and the treatment proposed is for mental disorder, then that Act may be used to override the attorney. The person could be treated under the Mental Health Act even if the attorney objects. However, this is not true for electro convulsive therapy (ECT) unless the emergency treatment powers of the Mental Health Act 1983 are being used (Sections 62(1A) or 64).
5. An attorney cannot demand treatment for the person they represent. However, they can challenge treatment decisions. If there is an objection by an attorney which cannot be resolved through discussion, an application should be made to the Court of Protection.

**Problems**

If an attorney is acting improperly, that is, contrary to a person's best interests or not following other requirements of the Act, staff should raise their concerns with the attorney directly or contact the Office of the Public Guardian. The Public Guardian has authority to investigate problems with attorneys and ultimately, they can refer a case to the Court of Protection to remove an attorney.

Office of the Public Guardian, PO Box 16185, Birmingham B2 2WH

Tel: 0300 456 0300 Fax: 0870 739 5780

Email: customerservices@publicguardian.gsi.gov.uk Website: www.gov.uk/office-of-public-guardian

**LPA Questions**

- *Can a lasting power of attorney (health and social care) refuse a DoLS authorisation?*

Yes. This would be a refusal. If the local authority believe the refusal is unreasonable (not in the person's best interests) they could challenge it via an application to the Court of Protection.

- *Can a lasting power of attorney (health and social care) authorise the detention of the person they represent?*

No. Only the DoLS procedures, Court of Protection order or Section 4B (to provide life sustaining treatment) can authorise a deprivation of liberty under the Mental Capacity Act. A lasting power of attorney can authorise restraint if the person lacks capacity but they are not able to authorise a deprivation of liberty.

- *If a property and affairs (financial) attorney refused to pay for the costs of a care home in which the local authority wanted to place a person under DoLS, would that effectively block a DoLS authorisation?*

No. This would not prevent the legal criteria of DoLS being met. However, it would present the local authority with a resource implication, at least in the short term. They would need to challenge the financial attorney's decision but it would not be enough to stop the person being placed under DoLS. It may be that court action would need to be taken later to recover the costs from the detained person's funds. If there is a significant dispute between the financial attorney and the local authority, it may be wise for the local authority to make an application to the Court of Protection promptly and before the placement.

## 3. Deputy

A personal welfare deputy may be appointed by the Court of Protection to make decisions on behalf of someone who lacks capacity to make decisions for themselves. If, in accordance with their authority, a deputy refuses some element of the proposed authorisation, the no refusals assessment will fail and the DoLS authorisation cannot be granted. It may be appropriate to remove a proposed condition to try and accommodate the deputy's objections so that the authorisation can then proceed. In the event there is concern that a deputy is acting contrary to a person's best interests, an application may be made to the Court of Protection to request the court removes the deputy's powers. If this is successful, a DoLS authorisation may then be used at a later date.

Only a deputy with health and welfare authority (personal welfare) can make a refusal for DoLS. This is relatively rare as the majority of deputies only have authority over finances (property and affairs).

**DoLS assessors**

In relation to deputies, DoLS assessors are required to:

1. ascertain whether a person has a deputy
2. check whether the person has a personal welfare (health and social care) deputy
3. determine whether the deputy (health and welfare) opposes the DoLS application.

In terms of the first point, the question a DoLS assessor will need to answer if challenged is what steps they took to confirm whether there was a deputy. A reasonable answer would include: a) asking the person being assessed b) speaking with staff of the care home or hospital c) checking the records of the care home or hospital d) speaking with family or other interested people e) checking the register of the Public Guardian (where it appears points a-d are not reliable, for example the person lacks capacity and has no family or friends).

It is important for the BIA to explain clearly to a deputy that they are being consulted because they can refuse a DoLS authorisation if they disagree with it. The BIA should directly ask the deputy if they oppose the proposed DoLS authorisation and record this on DoLS form 3 as otherwise they could claim they were merely consulted about the DoLS without being told of their right to refuse it.

A deputy will have a Court of Protection order stating their name and the name of the person who lacks capacity. The order will then state the extent of the deputy's authority. The DoLS assessor should ask to see this evidence. If they are concerned about the validity of the deputy's evidence, or the deputy cannot produce it, they can ask the Public Guardian to search the register of deputies. This is done by using Form OPG100 and it is a free service. A deputy order does not include photographic identification, so the only way of confirming that the person is the deputy they claim to be, would be to match their name to some other photographic identification such as a driving licence.

---

**Powers of deputies**

The deputy acts as an 'agent' for the person. Their powers are decided by the court and can be wide-ranging, including the management of all or part of the person's property, or more restrictive such as deciding on a particular financial transaction.

It should be noted that a deputy cannot:

1. override the person's decision if they have capacity in relation to that decision
2. prohibit someone from having contact with the person
3. change the individual who is responsible for the healthcare of the person
4. override the authority of an existing lasting power of attorney in areas where the attorney has authority
5. refuse consent to life-sustaining treatment.

## Mental Capacity Assessment

For DoLS to apply a person must lack the mental capacity to decide whether to stay in a care home or hospital for care or treatment. An assessment of their mental capacity therefore has to be undertaken. This assessment can be completed by either a mental health assessor or a best interests assessor. If a person is assessed as having capacity DoLS cannot be used. This means the person must be allowed to leave unless they consent to remaining in the care home or hospital. If they do not consent, the Mental Health Act 1983 may provide an option for keeping a person in a hospital, however the person would need to assessed under that Act.

In the latest annual DoLS figures[2], nearly 3,000 people were found to have mental capacity following assessment by an independent DoLS assessor. Without DoLS, it is most likely that those individuals would have been deprived of their liberty unlawfully with staff not recognising they had the mental capacity to decide where to live. It is important to note that the DoLS mental capacity assessment can be challenged in the Court of Protection. In some cases that have been before the Court of Protection it has been found that the assessments of mental capacity by DoLS assessors were inadequate and they were overruled (see page 50). A key requirement for anyone assessing mental capacity for DoLS is to show the evidence of a lack of mental capacity by reference to the legal criteria of the Act.

Further guidance for completion of DoLS Form 3 and 4 by assessors is given on page 127.

---

**Mental capacity assessment overview**

Section 2 of the Act defines a lack of mental capacity as follows:

> '*... a person lacks capacity in relation to a matter if at* ***the material time*** *he is unable to make a decision for himself* ***in relation to the matter*** *because of an* ***impairment of, or a disturbance*** *in the functioning of, the mind or brain.*'

The above definition contains a number of important elements that must be taken into account when deciding if a person lacks capacity.

---

**Time specific** (*the material time*)

A mental capacity assessment must be time specific. This recognises that mental capacity can fluctuate over time. In using the Act, staff must assess a person's mental capacity at the time a decision needs to be made. Once a person's capacity is assessed, it should not be presumed that it will remain the same indefinitely. With many conditions, a person's capacity to make decisions is not fixed. For example, people with a learning disability could see their capacity improve during their lifetime as they acquire new skills. In DoLS cases, there should be a request for a review if it is believed the person now has mental capacity.

---

**Decision specific** (*in relation to the matter*)

The decision DoLS assessors are required to assess, when undertaking a mental capacity assessment, is stated in the Act (Paragraph 15 Schedule A1 Part 3), it asks whether the person:

'*...lacks capacity in relation to the question whether or not he should be accommodated in the relevant hospital or care home for the purpose of being given the relevant care or treatment.*'

The assessor must consider what information is relevant to the decision regarding residence. This will then inform their discussion with the person they are assessing. What information a person needs to understand is considered in more detail on the next pages.

---

**Because of an impairment of, or a disturbance in the functioning of, the mind or brain**

The Act requires any incapacity to be *because of* an impairment of or disturbance in the functioning of the mind or brain. There must be a clear link between the impairment or disturbance and the inability to manage any of the four stages (understand, retain, use or weigh and communicate) of the assessment under Section 3 of the Act. An inability to do one of the parts *because of* hearing, sight, language or education would not result in a person being assessed as lacking mental capacity.

The Court of Appeal *(PC v City of York Council [2013] EWCA Civ 478)* stated that it is better to undertake the four stage functional mental capacity assessment (in Section 3 of the Act) first and then if the person was found to lack mental capacity, provide evidence of the link between the incapacity and the condition.

In the case of *Wandsworth CCG v IA [2014] EWCOP 990* the judge found the man concerned had mental capacity even though he had an acute brain injury and some '*difficult and inconsistent behaviours*'. The judge, with the assistance of expert evidence, found that these behaviours were present before the man's brain injury and therefore there was no evidence that he lacked mental capacity *because of* the brain injury. The judge stated:

*'I am conscious to guard against interpreting difficult and inconsistent behaviours ... as necessarily illustrative of a lack of capacity. Although IA can be very difficult at times, it is not right to infer that his resistance to, or simply lack of, compliance with care or treatment arises from an inability to understand, retain or use or weigh information. As Dr. Grace makes clear in her February 2013 report, 'it is important not to consider IA's non-concordance as arising solely from his Acute Brain Injury. The pattern of non-concordance was established prior to the injury in 2007'.*

---

**Assessing mental capacity** (Section 3)

This is a 'functional' assessment which looks at the decision making *process* rather than the outcome (the decision itself). In line with Act's definition of capacity, the assessment is time and decision specific. Accordingly, the assessor should apply the assessment and then decide whether the person has the mental capacity to make a particular decision at that particular time. There are four parts to the assessment and failure of any one part indicates a lack of mental capacity to make the specific decision in question at the particular time the decision needs to be made.

**To have capacity to make a decision a person must be able to:**

1. understand the information relevant to the decision *(including the reasonably foreseeable consequences of making or not making the decision)*
   **and**
2. retain that information *(long enough to make the decision)*
   **and**
3. use or weigh the information *(as part of the decision making process)*
   **and**
4. communicate the decision *(in any recognisable way)*

**1. Understand the information**

A person must be able to understand the *nature* of the decision (what), the *purpose* for which it is needed (why) and the *consequences* (risks and outcomes) of making the decision. In determining risks, the person only needs to consider what is reasonably foreseeable.

It is acceptable for the information to be understood in broad terms. In addition, case law indicates that the level of understanding does not have to be of a particularly high standard. The assessor will need to question the person to assess their understanding of the information given. It is for the assessor to judge how many questions are appropriate. For some people a simple open question will be sufficient to show the person understands the information presented whilst for other people, many questions will be needed to clarify their level of understanding.

<u>What information does a person need to understand?</u>

DoLS assessors need to consider what a person should understand. A starting point would be, whether the person understands:

1. what a care home or hospital is versus their own home or another place to live (nature)
2. that they have care needs which require support (purpose)
3. the risks or differences to them if they do not stay in a care home or hospital (consequences)

The Court of Protection has, in a number of cases, considered what 'salient factors' a person would need to understand to be resident for care or treatment. These provide useful guidance for DoLS assessors in their assessment of capacity. It is important to remember that these are not setting precedents and the information for each placement will vary depending on the specific placement and person being assessed. The cases do however provide a good indication of what the court's expectations are.

Mental health ward

In the case of *A Primary Care Trust v LDV & Others [2013] EWHC 272* the information considered relevant in relation to an admission to a hospital for mental health treatment was:

*'I consider that on the facts of this case, the clinicians ... should ask whether L has the capacity to understand, retain, use and weigh the following information:*

*(1) that she is in hospital to receive care and treatment for a mental disorder;*

*(2) that the care and treatment will include varying levels of supervision ... use of physical restraint and the prescription and administration of medication to control her mood;*

*(3) that staff will be entitled to carry out property and personal searches;*

*(4) that she must seek permission of the nursing staff to leave the hospital, and, until the staff at the hospital decide otherwise, she will only be allowed to leave under supervision;*

*(5) that if she left the hospital without permission and without supervision, the staff would take steps return her, including contacting the police.'*

Assessors need to ensure they provide a full picture of ward life, explaining both the restrictive and positive elements.

Supported living

In the case of *LBX v K, L & M [2013] EWHC 3230* the information considered relevant in relation to admission to a supported living placement was:

- the options available, the nature of the properties and their facilities
- the sort of area the properties were in (including any specific known risks)
- the difference between living somewhere and visiting it
- the activities the man would be able to do if he lived in each place
- whether and how regularly he would be able to see his family/friends if he lived in each place
- that he would need to pay money to live there
- that he would have to comply with the rules of each placement
- who he would be living within each placement
- the sort of care he would receive in each placement (including any differences to where he was living)

The judge also expressly set out what was not relevant: the cost of the placement and the value of money and the legal nature of the tenancy agreement or licence.

Although supported living is outside the DoLS regime, this case provides helpful guidance to assist DoLS assessors and those who complete the COPDOL10 form for judicial authorisations (see page 121).

Community rehabilitation placement

In the case of *Derbyshire County Council v AC [2014] EWCOP 38* the information considered relevant in relation to admission to a community rehabilitation placement was:

i) that the woman would live with other people
ii) that she would not live with her parents
iii) that she would be supported by workers
iv) the location of the placement
v) that she had considered the age and gender of the fellow residents
vi) that she would need to abide by house rules
vii) whether the placement was envisaged as long-term or as a short term placement

viii) in general terms, that one of the residential options has a therapeutic component

Before undertaking the assessment of capacity for DoLS, an assessor should be clear on these elements. They need to ascertain what the 'reasonably foreseeable' risks are for that individual and then consider what level of information they would need to understand these risks. The courts have repeatedly stated a person only needs to understand 'salient' points and not all peripheral details.

In the case of *CC v KK and STCC [2012] EWHC 2136* the judge was clear that, before assessment, the assessor needed to be clear on the options and the care package that would be available to the individual concerned if they were to go home as this was essential in order for them to understand the level of risk they would face if not living in a 24 hour staffed care home. The judge was critical of a doctor who started with a '*blank canvas'* when undertaking an assessment and asking the individual concerned to give him their *'ideal option'.*

If the person cannot understand the information relevant to the decision DoLS assessors need to show the evidence that led them to reach this conclusion.

Practicable steps

When assessing mental capacity, Principle 2 of the Act places a duty on staff to take all practicable steps to help the person during the assessment. The MCA Code of Practice (para 4.16) notes: '*Every effort must be made to provide information in a way that is most appropriate to help the person to understand'.* DoLS assessors need to clearly state the practicable steps they have taken to help a person when they assess capacity.

- *Question: What if a person does not know the reality of making a particular decision, for example, to live in a care home when they have never lived in one before?*

The assessor should give the person as much information as possible about the options perhaps by using pictures or photographs. In this particular example, wherever possible, a visit to the care home(s) would also be appropriate. However, it is important to remember that people will not know the reality of every decision they make until they experience the consequences of their actions. It is not vital to their understanding for them to have had the same experience previously.

---

## 2. Retain that information

The information for making a decision only has to be retained long enough to make the decision. There is not a set number of minutes or hours the person must remember information in order to pass the mental capacity assessment. The information could be forgotten an hour later and the decision would still be valid. It may be that if the person was presented with the same information an hour later, they would come to the same conclusion.

Practicable steps

If a person has problems retaining information, staff are obliged by Principle 2 of the Act to take practicable steps to help address this. The Code of Practice suggests using notebooks, photographs and voice recorders to help a person if they are struggling to retain information long enough to make a particular decision.

- *Question: What if someone gives different answers to the same decision at different times?*

The Act does not state that the assessment of capacity should be carried out several times so one assessment may be enough. However, if someone gives different answers to the same question at different times, it may be appropriate to do the assessment more than once. If the answer consistently changes, the assessor must consider whether the person is really able to retain the information and is truly using and weighing it. The assessor must also remember that a person has the right to change their mind or may simply be indecisive. Providing clear evidence of the assessment would be particularly important in such cases.

---

## 3. Use or weigh the information

A person must both understand information relating to a decision and also use and weigh that information. This means the person accepts the information and takes it into account. A number of court cases have examined this issue and they provide examples of when a person may understand information but they are not also able to use or weigh it and so lack capacity:

***Phobia/fear***
The panic or fear induced by a phobia may mean that a person is not able to use or weigh the information required. In this case, a pregnant woman with a needle phobia refused an anaesthetic needed for a caesarean section. The court ruled that at the point of treatment the needle phobia overwhelmed the woman and she was not able to use or weigh the information about the treatment and therefore lacked capacity at that time in relation to that particular treatment *(Re: MB (Caesarean Section) (1997) EWCA Civ 1361).*

***Delusions (misperception of reality)***
If a person has a misperception of reality then despite understanding information, they may not be able use or weigh the information as part of the decision making process. In this case, a person made an advance decision refusing a blood transfusion. They understood the need for blood and the risk of refusing blood but they refused it because they believed that their own blood was evil and would contaminate any new blood. The court ruled this was a misperception of reality and because the person was basing their decision on this misperception, they were not able to use or weigh the information about the transfusion *(T v NHS Trust [2004] EWHC 1279 (Fam)).*

The level and impact of a delusion on a decision must be considered however. In the case of *SB (A Patient; Capacity To Consent To Termination) [2013] EWHC 1417 (COP)* a judge decided that the woman concerned had sufficient mental capacity to decide to have a termination even though she had developed some delusional and paranoid beliefs about her husband and mother following her decision to stop taking medication for her mental disorder. Even though they were delusions which were relevant to the decision she had to make and it was accepted that they were influencing her decision, the judge decided that the extent to which they influenced her was not significant enough to outweigh or undermine the rest of her understanding and ability to use and weigh. The judge stated: '*It seems to me that this lady has made, and has maintained for an appreciable period of time, a decision. It may be that aspects of her reasons may be skewed by paranoia. There are other reasons which she has and which she has expressed. My own opinion is that it would be a total affront to the autonomy of this patient to conclude that she lacks capacity to the level required to make this decision.'*

***Insight***
In order to have capacity to give or refuse consent to treatment, the person needs to have insight into their illness. If a person does not accept they are ill, then despite understanding information about an illness and its treatment they will not be able to use or weigh this information as they do not believe they have an illness that needs treating. In this case, the person did not accept even the possibility that he might be mentally ill and thus in need of treatment for his mental disorder. The court ruled he lacked mental capacity to make treatment decisions related to his mental disorder *(R (B) v Dr SS [2006] EWCA Civ 28).*

Assessors would need to show how a lack of insight is impacting on a person's ability to make a decision. For example, some people with schizophrenia may not like the diagnostic label but still accept their symptoms and the treatment that alleviates these symptoms. A person in that position therefore could still have the mental capacity to consent to treatment for their mental health. In the case of *Heart of England NHS Foundation Trust v JB [2014] EWCOP 342* concerning a woman with schizophrenia and whether she had capacity to decide about surgery on her leg the judge noted: *'...there is no necessary correlation between a lack of insight into schizophrenia and incapacity to decide about surgery'.* The judge concluded she did have capacity regarding the surgery.

***Memory loss***
If a person has a problem with memory loss this could mean they cannot use or weigh key information during the decision making process. In the case of *Westminster City Council v Sykes [2014] EWHC B9* which concerned a woman with dementia the judge noted: *'...she cannot recall the circumstances and behaviour that caused others to remove her from her own home to hospital and to transfer her to residential care. Lacking this information, she does not accept that she had significant problems at home, nor therefore that she requires a significant package of care and support.'*

***Compulsive disorders***
The MCA Code of Practice (para 4.22) notes: '*... a person with the eating disorder anorexia nervosa may understand information about the consequences of not eating. But their compulsion not to eat might be too strong for them to ignore.'* Another example of a compulsive disorder affecting the ability to use or weigh information is Prader-Willi Syndrome which involves compulsive overeating.

***Impulsivity***
The MCA Code of Practice (para 4.22) also identifies impulsivity as a factor that may affect a person's ability to use or weigh information as follows: '*Some people who have serious brain damage might make impulsive decisions regardless of information they have been given or their understanding of it.'*

Practicable steps

If a person has problems using or weighing the information, staff are obliged by Principle 2 of the Act to take practicable steps to address this. Such steps could include using someone the person trusts to give the information or giving the person more time to enable them to think about the information more carefully.

---

### 4. Communicate the decision

A person can communicate their decision using any method recognised by those undertaking the assessment, for example by hand signals, gestures or other behaviour. The Code of Practice (para 4.25) states: '*Communication by simple muscle movements can show that somebody can communicate and may have capacity to make a decision*'.

Practicable steps

If a person has problems communicating, staff are obliged by Principle 2 of the Act to take practicable steps to help address this. Those undertaking the assessment could use a specialist worker (speech and language therapist), family or friends to ensure that a person's capacity is not incorrectly judged simply because the assessor could not recognise their means of communication.

---

### The burden of proof and reasonable belief

When assessing capacity, the burden of proof rests with the person assessing capacity. The person being assessed does not have to prove they have capacity. In the case of *CC v KK [2012] EWCOP 2136* the judge noted: '*First, a person must be assumed to have capacity unless it is established that she lacks capacity: s. 1(2). The burden of proof therefore lies on the party asserting that P does not have capacity.'*

To reach a conclusion, based on the assessment of capacity, it is sufficient that the assessor holds a '*reasonable belief*' that someone either has or lacks capacity with regard to the decision. Absolute certainty is not therefore required and in many cases it would be impossible to attain such certainty. The relevant legal test (or standard of proof) requires that the assessor makes a judgment on the balance of probabilities, or in other words, what is more likely than not.

---

### Risk

The Act clearly states (Section 1(4)) that a person is not to be judged as lacking mental capacity simply because they have made an unwise decision. The process of decision making should be judged instead of the decision they come to. If an adult has mental capacity, they can make risky decisions as long as they understand and accept the consequences of the decision. In the case of *CC v KK [2012] EWCOP 2136* an 82 year old woman wanted to live at home and accepted the limitations of living there. However, she had previously used a lifeline alarm over 1,000 times within the space of six months due to anxiety at night. A number of professionals assessed her as lacking mental capacity to decide where to live. Their assessments focussed on her using the lifeline service and the fact that she could not understand the impact on the service or others even though she was also able to describe the level of support and care she needed in her own home and acknowledged the risks of living there.

In relation to the use of the lifeline alarm, KK said: *'I understand why this was inappropriate and consider my behaviour in using it so much to have been silly ... I was nervous ... but I have learnt my lesson.'* About returning to live in her bungalow, she said: *'Everything I've got is in that bungalow. My whole life. Everything is familiar to me. I've got my hobbies ... If I die on the floor, I die on the floor. I'd rather die in my own bungalow, I really would.'*

Based on the evidence, the judge felt she understood the care and support she needed in her own home and was realistic in her assessment of her own abilities. The judge stated: *'There is, I perceive, a danger that professionals, including judges, may objectively conflate a capacity assessment with a best interests analysis and conclude that the person under review should attach greater weight to the physical security and comfort of a residential home and less importance to the emotional security and comfort that the person derives from being in their own home ... I perceive a real danger that in assessing KK's capacity professionals and the court may consciously or subconsciously attach excessive weight to their own views of how her physical safety may be best protected and insufficient weight to her own view of how her emotional needs may best be met.'*

---

**Refusal to be assessed**

The MCA Code of Practice (para 4.57-4.59) advises that where a person is unable to engage fully but is compliant with the assessment process, and staff believe it is in the person's best interests to enable them to make a decision, then it would be appropriate to carry out an assessment. However, if a person is unwilling to engage in the process and appears to have capacity, they can refuse to be assessed under the Act and no assessment can take place. In some cases, it may be appropriate to seek legal advice and ultimately obtain a declaration from the Court of Protection in relation to the person's capacity if there is some evidence of incapacity but staff are unable to properly assess this.

---

**Discrimination due to mental disorder**

On occasion, the courts have considered people to be assessed more harshly because the assessors are aware they have a mental disorder so that what they say is not taken at face value even though there is no link between their mental disorder and the alleged incapacity. In the case of *PH v A Local Authority & Z Limited & R [2011] EWHC 1704*, the judge stated: *'...courts must guard against imposing too high a test of capacity to decide issues such as residence because to do so would run the risk of discriminating against persons suffering from a mental disability.'*

In *Heart of England NHS Foundation Trust v JB [2014] EWCOP 342* the judge noted: *'...JB's schizophrenia is relevant to the way in which she decides, and not to her capacity to decide. Her tendency at times to be uncommunicative or avoidant and to minimise the risks of inaction are understandable human ways of dealing with her predicament and do not amount to incapacity.'*

---

**Indecision**

In the case of *Heart of England NHS Foundation Trust v JB [2014] EWCOP 342,* the woman concerned (JB), was faced with a difficult decision about whether to consent to an amputation. Some of the professionals assessing JB's mental capacity considered that she lacked capacity and pointed to her chronic schizophrenia as being the cause. In fact, the judge considered that she was simply struggling to make a decision which would probably be true of anyone in her position: *'It must also be remembered that common strategies for dealing with unpalatable dilemmas – for example indecision, avoidance or vacillation – are not to be confused with incapacity. We should not ask more of people whose capacity is questioned than of those whose capacity is undoubted.'*

---

**Coercion and undue influence**

It may be that a person lacks capacity due to coercion or undue influence. This is where a person is under such pressure by another individual, or group, that they cannot make a free choice. This is not a type of incapacity that falls within the scope of the Mental Capacity Act as it is not caused by an *impairment or disturbance in the functioning of the mind or brain* (although a person may be more susceptible to coercion because of such a condition). For example, an assessor may assess a person with dementia who lacks capacity to decide where to live not *because of* their dementia but because of undue pressure from their adult children to live in a certain place. Assessors therefore need to establish the cause of a person's lack of capacity.

Cases involving coercion or undue influence should be referred to the High Court to be dealt with under its inherent jurisdiction *(DL v A Local Authority EWCA [2012] Civ 253).* Local authorities have safeguarding duties to investigate concerns regarding vulnerable people who are being coerced and sometimes this will lead to court applications to take further action.

---

**Age, appearance, condition or behaviour**

The legislation states that a lack of capacity cannot be decided merely by reference to a person's age, appearance, condition or behaviour. The MCA Code of Practice (para 4.8) notes that 'appearance' includes: '*... the physical characteristics of certain conditions (for example, scars, features linked to Down's syndrome or muscle spasms caused by cerebral palsy) as well as aspects of appearance like skin colour, tattoos and body piercings, or the way people dress (including religious dress).*'

---

**Practice points for DoLS assessors**

1. Have you supported the person with practical steps? Are there any that you thought of but could not implement? Have you explained why?
2. Remember not to judge the person's mental capacity on how wise their decision is. You must focus on their process of reasoning.
3. Have you provided evidence of a link between the person's incapacity and their mental disorder?
4. Remember just because a person is optimistic, uncommunicative, difficult to engage or indecisive does not necessarily mean they lack mental capacity.
5. Did you present the person with clear options? This might require more than one visit because the options might be unclear initially.
6. Did you talk about the positives and negatives of both options? Remember a person does not have to understand everything about the decision, just the key facts.
7. If you believe a person cannot understand or weigh risks, have you recorded what these risks are and what you believe they cannot understand?
8. Do not copy and paste information from previous assessments. The gravity of the issue for the person possibly being deprived of liberty necessitates the right to a fresh mental capacity assessment every time.
9. Remember you have to prove the person lacks capacity. They do not have to prove anything. It may be useful to have verbatim quotes of what the person has said to you in response to your questions as evidence for finding they lack capacity.

---

**Frequently asked questions**

- *How do you know whether the person has really understood? What if they simply give the responses they think you want to hear?*

The capacity assessment is not a scientific assessment and the law recognises this. The assessment is based on the balance of probabilities (what is more likely than not). In accordance with many decisions made by health and social care staff, the capacity assessment requires a judgment to be made based on the available evidence. It is particularly important to ask open questions and ask the person to convey back what they have understood.

- *How do you approach the capacity assessment if someone misusing alcoholic and also has a brain injury or other mental disorder?*

What needs to be identified is whether the person's mental capacity is being impaired by the brain injury (or other mental disorder) or whether their decision making is simply impaired in the way it would be with a person who is misusing alcohol due to addiction. This is important in DoLS cases because someone with a brain injury which is changing their behaviour could be deprived of their liberty under DoLS but not if they were simply misusing alcohol. In the case of *RB v Brighton & Hove City Council [2014] EWCA Civ 561*, the judge had to hear evidence and decide between the two potential causes of RB's incapacity. RB's barrister argued that '*...the frontal lobe damage is not the cause of RB's inability to weigh up and use relevant information.....the difference between RB's present condition and that of an alcoholic without brain injury is "wafer thin"*'. However, the Court of Appeal considered the medical evidence showed that RB's inability to use and weigh was because of the brain injury and therefore the mental capacity assessment for DoLS was satisfied. The court further stated it was in RB's best interests to remain under DoLS in a care home.

- *What if the person's capacity to decide whether to stay in the care home or hospital fluctuates regularly?*

The DoLS Code of Practice (para 8.24) gives guidance on this issue *'Where there is consistent evidence of regaining capacity on this longer-term basis, deprivation of liberty should be lifted immediately, and a formal review and termination of the authorisation sought. However, it should be borne in mind that a deprivation of liberty authorisation carries with it certain safeguards that the relevant person will lose if the authorisation is terminated. Where the regaining of capacity is likely to be temporary, and the authorisation will be required again within a short period of time, the authorisation should be left in place, but with the situation kept under ongoing review.'*

- *Do you have to tell a person you are assessing their capacity?*

Yes. If a person has capacity they can refuse to take part in the assessment. It is also important to let a person know you are assessing their capacity because they may be able to suggest 'practicable steps' to help them with the test.

- *What if a person can understand the risks of making a particular decision but do not accept that it will actually happen to them?*

It will depend on why they believe it will not happen to them. If a person accepts, in principle, that a possible consequence of a proposed treatment is that 10% of people die but the person does not believe they will be in this 10%, due consideration should be given to a person's optimism or perhaps their religious faith as long as they accept death is a possible result. However, if a person refuses to accept the consequences will apply to them because of a delusional belief such as they are immortal, then they are likely to be assessed as lacking capacity about giving or refusing consent to the treatment.

## Best Interests Assessment

The best interests assessment is the most detailed of the DoLS assessments. Its importance was underlined in the case of *London Borough of Hillingdon v Neary & Anor [2011] EWCOP 1377* where the judge stated:

*'...the best interests assessment is anything but a routine piece of paperwork. Properly viewed, it should be seen as a cornerstone of the protection that the DOL safeguards offer to people facing deprivation of liberty if they are to be effective as safeguards at all.'*

A DoLS best interests assessor (BIA) has to complete the assessment which contains four criteria that the person must meet:

1. **They are (or will be) deprived of their liberty in a care home or hospital.**
2. **It is in their best interests to be deprived of their liberty there.**
3. **It is necessary in order to prevent harm to them that they are deprived of their liberty.**
4. **Deprivation of liberty is a proportionate response to the seriousness and the likelihood of harm.**

In addition, the assessment requires the BIA to recommend the maximum time period (duration) for the standard DoLS authorisation which can be up to one year. They can also recommend that conditions (see page 73) be attached. The BIA must consult people close to the person (including advocates) and the legislation (Paragraph 39 Schedule A1) states they must also:

a) consult the care home or hospital

b) have regard to the conclusions of the mental health assessor about the impact of the deprivation of liberty upon the person

c) have regard to any relevant needs assessment and care plan.

Guidance on the completion of Form 3 by best interests assessors is given on page 127.

---

### 1. They are (or will be) deprived of their liberty in a care home or hospital

This question is considered on pages 15. Although it is likely that many people in care homes who lack the mental capacity to consent to being there will meet the *acid test*, it is important that BIAs provide evidence to support their conclusion that the person is (or will be) deprived of their liberty.

---

### 2. It is in their best interests to be deprived of their liberty there

If a person is assessed as lacking capacity to make a specific decision, the Act allows another person to make a best interests decision on their behalf. Section 4 of the Mental Capacity Act provides a checklist that must be followed when making a best interests decision on behalf of another person thereby ensuring a uniform approach by staff and, in the case of DoLS, the assessors. The checklist (listed overleaf) represents the minimum that should be considered when making a best interests decision. Other factors can be added to it as appropriate under the heading *'all relevant circumstances'*. It is important to note that what is in a person's best interests under the Act may be different to what is in their best clinical interests.

The balance sheet approach

The courts use a balance sheet approach to decide what is in a person's best interests. This includes a consideration of both positive and negative issues related to a decision. This means best interests assessors and other decision makers under the Act should ensure that their assessment shows a balanced approach. A one sided assessment may lead to a challenge. In addition, the balance sheet method provides evidence that a best interests assessor has not decided the outcome before completing the assessment. The assessment process should inform their decision.

An unbalanced approach was identified in the case of *AH v Hertfordshire NHS Trust [2011] EWHC 276.* The judge believed that staff had already made a decision and wanted to fit their best interests record keeping to that predetermined decision: *'The MCA Code of Practice may be stating the obvious when it says at paragraph 5.13 that 'it is important not to take shortcuts in working out best interests and a proper and objective assessment must be carried out on every occasion'.* He noted that: *'Ealing had never conducted a baseline balance-sheet exercise about whether it was in Alan's interests to move or not. Its assessments had either been conducted on the assumption that he would one day have to move, or took the form of arguments justifying a decision already taken.'*

The best interests 'checklist'

To make a best interests decision the decision maker must consider or take the following steps:

- All relevant circumstances
- If the person will have capacity sometime in the future in relation to the matter?
- The person's reasonably ascertainable past and present wishes and feelings
- The person's beliefs and values.
- Any other factors the person would consider if able to do so
- Consult as practicable and appropriate the following people:
  - who are involved in the care of the person
  - have an interest in the welfare of the person (ie relatives, advocates, friends)
  - anyone the person has already named
  - any attorneys or deputies
- As far as reasonably practicable encourage and permit the person to participate
- Consider less restrictive options in terms of the person's rights and freedom of action
- Must not base the decision solely on age, appearance, behaviour or condition.
- Must not be motivated by a desire to bring about the person's death if the decision is about life-sustaining treatment

- **All relevant circumstances**

Relevant circumstances are those that the person making the decision is aware of or could reasonably be expected to be aware of. This could include the best clinical or medical decision given the patient's condition, their history, care needs, risk assessments, age, diagnosis and/or prognosis and resources available in terms of local services or funding.

The Court of Appeal in *R (K) v Camden and Islington Health Authority [2001] EWCA Civ 240* accepted that if a public body tries its best to obtain care for a person in a community setting but the required level of care is not available this may lead to someone being deprived of their liberty. Nevertheless they concluded the deprivation of liberty could still be legal: *'If a Health Authority is unable, despite the exercise of all reasonable endeavours, to procure for a patient the level of care and treatment in the community that a Tribunal considers to be a prerequisite to the discharge of the patient from hospital, I do not consider that the continued detention of the patient in hospital will violate the right to liberty conferred by Article 5.'*

The actual services or care available may be limited due to budgetary constraints. In the case of *Re: MN (An adult) [2015] EWCA Civ 411* the Court of Appeal decided that there was no need to consider 'hypothetical' best interests options which were not going to be made available by the local authority: *'The Court of Protection is thus confined to choosing between available options, including those which there is good reason to believe will be forthcoming in the foreseeable future.'* It continued: '*... in the final analysis the Court of Protection cannot compel a public authority to agree to a care plan which the authority is unwilling to implement.'*

The application of this judgment to cases involving a deprivation of liberty has however been questioned very recently in the case of *North Yorkshire County Council v MAG & Ors [2015] EWCOP 64.* In this more recent case, a man had been placed in a flat for nine years which was so small that he could not mobilise using a wheelchair and so had to resort to crawling and pulling himself along the floor and up on to chairs and his bed. All parties and the judge agreed the man concerned was deprived of his liberty. The judge felt that the local authority had not adequately explored less restrictive options and given that the case involved a deprivation of liberty stated: *'This is a question of MAG's liberty and I do not accept that I can authorise the deprivation of that liberty on the basis that nothing else is available. He has been in this unsatisfactory situation for a prolonged period. NYCC has been extremely slow to accept its responsibilities in relation to rehousing him.'* Given this, the judge refused to authorise the continued deprivation of liberty of the man involved.

An alternative legal remedy for a person who feels there has been insufficient funding committed to their care may be a judicial review and/or a human rights challenge. The case of *McDonald v UK [2014] ECHR 942* concerned the lack of provision of night carers to assist a woman to go to the toilet. It was considered a breach of her Article 8 ECHR right to respect for private and family life.

---

- **If the person will have capacity sometime in the future in relation to the matter?**

This is a safeguard in cases where a person may regain capacity and consequently be able to make their own decisions. Best interests assessors need to consider if the person's condition is such that their capacity could improve or treatment could have an effect. It may be necessary to speak to the mental health assessor to discuss this and consider a shorter authorisation in these cases.

---

- **The person's reasonably ascertainable past and present wishes and feelings**

The legislation uses the phrase *reasonably ascertainable past and present wishes and feelings.* These can be expressed verbally or in writing and can include emotional responses and other behaviour. The MCA Code of Practice (para 5.39) states that reasonably ascertainable means: *'... considering all possible information in the time available. What is available in an emergency will be different to what is available in a non-emergency.'*

The DoLS Code of Practice (para 4.70) states: *'The BIA will need to consider the conclusions of the mental health assessor about how the person being assessed is likely to be affected by being deprived of their liberty. If the proposed care would involve the person being moved, then the assessor should consider the impact of the upheaval and of the journey itself on the person.'*

If a person made any verbal or written statements when they had capacity, indicating their wishes in relation to the decision, these should be considered carefully and if they are not followed, the reasons recorded. A written statement sometimes known as an advance directive or advance statement, *requesting* treatment or care is different to an advance decision which states a *refusal* of treatment. An advance decision is legally binding if it is valid and applicable to the circumstances. See the No Refusals Assessment chapter earlier.

Giving weight to wishes and feelings

In the case of *ITW v Z & M [2009] EWHC 2525,* the judge gave the following guidance:

1. The nearer a person is to having capacity the greater the weight should be given to their views.
2. Regard must be had to both the strength and consistency of the person's views.
3. Weight must be given to the impact on the person of knowing that their wishes are not going to be met.
4. The extent to which the wishes are rational, sensible, practical must be considered.

In *Re M (Best Interests: Deprivation of Liberty) [2013] EWHC 3456 (COP)* the judge noted that although it was accepted a woman placed in a care home lacked capacity, her assessment of her quality of life was an important consideration in determining her best interests. The judge stated that when considering best interests, just keeping people alive longer is not necessarily enough to ensure their best interests are properly served: *'In the end, if M remains confined in a home she is entitled to ask "What for?" The only answer that could be provided at the moment is "To keep you alive as long as possible". In my view that is not a sufficient answer. The right to life and the state's obligation to protect it is not absolute and the court must surely have regard to the person's own assessment of her quality of life. In M's case there is little to be said for a solution that attempts, without any guarantee of success, to preserve for her a daily life without meaning or happiness and which she with some justification, regards as insupportable.'*
The judge noted that because the best interests decision about where she should live was so finely balanced, it was right that the matter was decided by a court: *'... my decision implies no criticism*

*whatever of any of the witnesses from the local authority or by the CCG. I understand the position taken and the reasons for it; indeed it would be difficult for them to have taken a different view on the facts of the case. There are risks either way and it is perfectly appropriate that responsibility for the outcome should fall on the shoulders of the court and not on the shoulders of the parties.'*

In another case *(Wye Valley NHS Trust v B (Rev 1) [2015] EWCOP 60)* the Court of Protection had to consider the case of a 73 year old man who refused for his foot to be amputated because of complications as a result of diabetes. He had been diagnosed with a mental disorder in his 20s and had long standing delusions based in religion affecting his capacity to make different decisions and he was judged to lack the mental capacity about the proposed amputation. The judge stated however that when it came to the best interests assessment those beliefs must not be ignored: *'His religious beliefs are deeply meaningful to him and do not deserve to be described as delusions: they are his faith and they are an intrinsic part of who he is. I would not define Mr B by reference to his mental illness or his religious beliefs. Rather, his core quality is his "fierce independence", and it is this that is now, as he sees it, under attack.'*

The judge decided that these wishes should be given significant weight especially as the man had little time left to live and if the amputation was enforced it would be a constant reminder that his wishes had been overridden. He noted that in relation to stated wishes, although a person may lack capacity, their wishes and feelings should not be discounted. The judge weighed up the infringement on the man's autonomy against the objective of treating his medical condition and decided that: *'... it would not be in Mr B's best interests to take away his little remaining independence and dignity in order to replace it with a future for which he understandably has no appetite and which could only be achieved after a traumatic and uncertain struggle that he and no one else would have to endure.'*

These cases are a reminder that for the courts, best interests are not simply about medical best interests, lowest risk or the safest option. Best interests looks at the whole situation with the person at the centre. However, it is worth noting that it is not currently the position in law that a person's best interests must always be the same as what they wanted when they had mental capacity. The person's prior wishes must be given weight but they are only part of the equation. In some cases, the BIA may feel the decision between weighing up risks and the person's wishes and feelings is so finely balanced that they recommend the case is decided by the Court of Protection and propose a short duration for the standard DoLS authorisation to allow for an application to be made to the court.

---

- **The person's beliefs and values**

Beliefs and values can include a person's religious, cultural and lifestyle beliefs and consideration of how these may have influenced the decision the person would have made for themselves. These may extend to political influences, charities the person had supported or religious groups they belonged to even if not a major world religion. What is important to consider is the person's strength of belief and see if it is relevant to the overall decision.

In the case *Westminster City Council v Sykes [2014] EWCOP B9* the Court of Protection considered the case of a woman who had been a passionate campaigner throughout her life. The judge felt that the way she had lived her life was a factor in determining her best interests. He stated: '... *Ms S has had a dramatic life, and the drama is not yet over. She has played a part in many of the moral, political and ideological battles of the twentieth century ... by nature she is a fighter, a campaigner, a person of passion. She appears always to have placed herself in the public eye, in the mainstream ... causing, accepting and courting controversy.'*

In deciding that she should be allowed to return home, as she wanted, for a trial even though there were a number of risks, he concluded that: '...*MS's personality is a critical factor. She has always wished to be heard. She would wish her life to end with a bang not a whimper.'*

In another case the Court of Protection *(A NHS Trust & B PCT v DU, AO, EB & AU [2009] EWHC 3504)* considered the future care and treatment of an 86 year old Nigerian woman who was very unwell and in need of 24 hour care. There was a dispute between her family and the general hospital treating her about her best medical interests and ultimately whether returning to Nigeria was in her best interests. The judge stated: '*It is an integral part of the concept of best interests when dealing with a person of this age that the court recognises the imminent possibility of death and the importance of making arrangements so as to secure that the experience of death may be in a context which is the most congenial and peaceful that can be devised. Also implicit in the concept of best interests is the importance of the country and culture of origin and the whereabouts of the family. They will often take precedence over, for example, the question of risk avoidance or the exact quality of care that may be available.'*

Best interests assessors therefore need to consider their assessment of the person as a whole. Even if the person has not made any prior statements a BIA should consider their lifestyle, the force of the person's convictions and the way they lived previously. These should be recorded where relevant in the DoLS assessment.

What if the person objects to a deprivation of liberty?

In the case of *C v Blackburn and Darwen Borough Council [2011] EWHC 3321,* Mr Justice Jackson stated that: '... *genuinely contested issues about the place of residence of a resisting incapacitated person ... ought properly to be made by the Court of Protection, using its power to make welfare decisions under s16 MCA.'* This has been repeated in the more recent cases of *AJ v A Local Authority [2015] EWCOP 5* and also *Essex County Council v RF & Ors [2015] EWCOP 1* which both stress the importance of access to the Court of Protection in cases of deprivation of liberty. If a best interests assessor notes the person is objecting to being in the care home or hospital during the assessment process, they should notify the relevant local authority as a matter of urgency so that appropriate steps can be taken to apply to the Court of Protection for a hearing. The application must be made promptly either by the representative, an IMCA or directly by the local authority.

---

- **Any other factors the person would consider if able to do so**

Any other factors can include anything that the decision maker considers relevant. The MCA Code of Practice (para 5.47) notes: *'This might include the effect of the decision on other people, obligations to dependants or the duties of a responsible citizen.'* The best interests assessment recognises that people with capacity often consider various factors when they make decisions rather than only considering medical or financial issues. For example, a person with a terminal illness may choose treatment options which reduce possible life expectancy but give them a better quality of life.

---

- **Consult others as practicable and appropriate to do so**

The Act places a legal obligation on decision makers (in this case DoLS best interests assessors) to consult others, but only if it is practicable and appropriate to do so. Consultation can take many forms including telephone conversations, personal interviews and email correspondence.

Practicable and appropriate means that although consultation of others is an obligation under the Act, it can be overridden in certain situations. In some circumstances, it may be practicable to consult a relative but not appropriate to do so because they have not been in contact with the person for some time and show no interest in their welfare. It is for the BIA to consider if consultation with any person is practicable or appropriate at the time. In DoLS cases, there may be a need for an urgent authorisation to be extended when the BIA cannot contact the family within the seven day period.

Any number of people can be consulted if they are appropriate. The legislation does not dictate a hierarchy of people to be consulted or exclude specific people from consultation, although there is a list of *'interested persons'* (see below). However, the Act states that any person with an interest in the welfare of the individual concerned can be consulted. This could include relatives, carers, friends or a neighbour visiting the person regularly. DoLS assessors must show they have thought carefully about who to speak to or not and it is important to record the reasoning.

When considering the weight of others' views, the following factors are relevant:

- How long have they known the person and what is their relationship with them?
- How much interest have they shown in the person?
- How much contact do they have with them?
- Is there a potential conflict interest which could influence their view?

The Act provides (Paragraph 185 of Schedule A1) a list of *'interested'* people the DoLS assessor should consult as part of the best interests assessment:

- Spouse or civil partner (or those living together as husband and wife or civil partners)
- Children and step children

- Parents and step parents
- Brothers and sisters (including half or step brothers and sisters)
- Grandparents
- Deputy
- Attorney

Paragraph 186 Schedule A1 states the duty to consult does not apply if the BIA: *'(a) is not aware of the interested person's identity or of a way of contacting him, and (b) cannot reasonably ascertain it.'*

**Note:** If a person has no one who is appropriate to consult with during the best interests assessment, an advocate (IMCA) must be arranged for them by the local authority (see page 79).

Although the DoLS assessor has a duty to consult and take into account the views of other people this does not mean they must follow what is said by those consulted if, in the assessor's opinion, their views are not in the person's best interests (but please see case of *Steven Neary* below). The main objective of consultation is to try and establish the views, wishes, beliefs and values of the person who lacks capacity and what they would have done if they were still able to make their own decisions. The Code of Practice (para 5.67) notes that people who have a potential conflict of interest should still be consulted. For example, the beneficiary of a will should not automatically be excluded from consultation. However, the best interests assessor may need to decide whether the potential conflict of interest means the person is giving a biased view of what is in the person's best interests.

The obligation on staff to consult others has an impact upon confidentiality. Staff should ensure they balance the duty to consult with a patient's right to confidentiality. They will need to refer to other law, policy and professional guidance on this subject. The MCA Code of Practice provides guidance on this issue in chapter 16. An important consideration will be assessing the person's capacity to consent to consultation with those closest to them.

The case of *London Borough of Hillingdon v Neary & Anor [2011] EWCOP 1377* made it clear that if the deprivation of liberty is against the wishes of interested and concerned family members, the matter should be brought before the Court of Protection and DoLS should not be used as a way for local authorities to override the views of those closest to the person. DoLS does not provide permission to interfere with the right to respect for a private and family life under Article 8 of the European Convention on Human Rights.

Consulting the mental health assessor

The DoLS Code of Practice (para 4.39) states: '*The mental health assessor is required to consider how the mental health of the person being assessed is likely to be affected by being deprived of their liberty, and to report their conclusions to the best interests assessor.'* The legislation (Paragraph 39 Schedule A1) places a duty on BIAs to have regard to the conclusions of the mental health assessor.

---

- **As far as reasonably practicable encourage and permit the person to participate**

Even when a person lacks capacity, they should not be excluded from the decision making process. For example, where possible, the person should be brought into any care planning meeting where a best interests decision is being made on their behalf. If the person would be unhappy in such a meeting or it might cause them distress, other ways for them to participate should be considered. In the case of a person being placed in residential care they could be taken to different homes to observe their response (even if only gestures or facial expressions) which could be taken into account when considering their best interests.

---

- **Consider less restrictive options in terms of the person's rights and freedom of action**

Principle 5 of the Act states that any best interests decision should consider less restrictive options in terms of a person's rights and freedoms. There may be an alternative way of acting which is just (or nearly) as effective but less restrictive. The decision maker must also consider whether it is necessary to act at all. However there may be many decisions made for people who lack capacity which are not less restrictive but, due to other factors in the best interests assessment, they are applied. Limitations in funding could be one such factor as the Act does not oblige authorities to spend beyond their budgets. However, see the notes under *'relevant circumstances'* above for recent case law about this.

The case of *London Borough of Hillingdon v Neary & Anor [2011] EWCOP 1377* highlighted the need for BIAs to consider less restrictive options in DoLS cases. The BIAs in this case failed to record less restrictive options such as the option to return Steven back to the care of his father. The judge criticised this failing (and several others) and concluded the DoLS authorisations issued were unlawful as the best interests assessments on which they were based were flawed.

It is important that best interests assessors present evidence of their consideration of less restrictive options and the reasons as to why they were not chosen if this is the case. In addition BIAs should not automatically just discount unrealistic options suggested by family or friends of a person. They need to show they have considered them and the reasons why they were or were not chosen.

---

- **Must not base the decision solely on age, appearance, behaviour or condition**

A best interests decision cannot be based *solely* on the age, appearance, condition or behaviour of the person lacking capacity. However, these factors may have some relevance as part of the overall best interests assessment. For example, the fact a person is 85 and has dementia is a relevant circumstance in relation to choosing the most appropriate residential placement. The MCA Code of Practice explains (para 4.8 and 4.9) that the term *'appearance'* includes physical appearance such as skin colour, clothes and visible disabilities. *'Condition'* includes physical disability, learning disability, unconsciousness or confusion from drug or alcohol misuse.

---

- **Must not be motivated by a desire to bring about the person's death if the decision is about life-sustaining treatment**

In treatment matters, this principle is designed to protect people lacking capacity but it does not mean that doctors are obliged to provide or continue life-sustaining treatment if that treatment is not in the best interests of the person.

---

**Disputes**

Some decisions will be complicated because they involve conflicting views from those involved. In such cases, the BIA should try and reach a consensus and record the varying views of interested persons. However, in cases where close relatives or friends of the person lacking capacity, who are concerned with their welfare, are unhappy with the decision, the local authority, NHS Trust or CCG must be proactive and approach the court themselves and must not use DoLS as a way of overriding these views.

**Protection for the decision-maker**

By applying the best interests checklist the best interests assessor and other decision makers are protected by the Act. The legislation states it is sufficient for the decision-maker to have a *'reasonable belief'* about the person's best interests and this belief should be based on the balance of probabilities (what is more likely than not). The decision may be discovered, with hindsight, not to have been the best decision within Section 4 and the BIA or other decision maker may be challenged. However, they should be protected as long as they are able to show they followed the checklist, acted within the boundaries of the legislation and had a reasonable belief about their decision.

It is important to note that, under the Act, a person is not protected from liability for loss or damage as a result of negligence in carrying out actions for those lacking capacity.

---

### 3. It is necessary in order to prevent harm to them that they are deprived of their liberty

It is notable that harm to *others* is not covered by DoLS in the same way that it is not covered under the Mental Capacity Act's powers of restraint. Where harm to others necessitates deprivation of liberty, the Mental Health Act 1983 may be an option if the person meets the criteria of that Act.

The Mental Capacity Act gives no information as to the nature of harm that could be considered to qualify for an authorisation. It is suggested however that where possible, an appropriate risk assessment tool is used to quantify and record the potential harm the person faces.

The DoLS Code of Practice (para 4.61) states the following factors should be considered:

- *'whether any harm to the person could arise if the deprivation of liberty does not take place,*
- *what that harm would be,*
- *how likely that harm is to arise (i.e. is the level of risk sufficient to justify a step as serious as depriving a person of liberty?)*
- *what other care options there are which could avoid deprivation of liberty, and*
- *if deprivation of liberty is currently unavoidable, what action could be taken to avoid it in future'*

Harm to others and DoLS

In the case of *Y County Council v ZZ [2012] EWHC B34*, the judge decided to impose limitations which at first glance may have appeared to be for the protection of others but in fact, the judge was able to explain how they were in the best interests of the man concerned. The aim of the restrictions was to prevent him suffering assaults in retaliation for his behaviour and being investigated by the police; both of which he would not have understood and would have caused him considerable distress. The judge stated as: *'...I make it clear to Mr ZZ that I have no doubt that the restrictions upon him are in his best interests. They are designed to keep him out of mischief, to keep him safe and healthy, to keep others safe, to prevent the sort of situation where the relative of a child wanted to do him serious harm, which I have no doubt was very frightening for him, and they are there to prevent him from getting into serious trouble with the police.'*

---

### 4. Deprivation of liberty is a proportionate response to the seriousness and the likelihood of harm

A proportionate response is one that involves the minimum control for the shortest possible time. The best interests assessor should consider whether there are less restrictive, and therefore more proportionate actions that could be taken to protect the person in order to avoid a deprivation of liberty. In terms of seriousness and likelihood, a best interests assessor will need to consider evidence of the risk of harm in the care plan and whether the person had come to harm before and how likely they might again. It would be important to have specific examples rather than general statements, for example, the number of falls a person might have had in their own home over a particular period of time rather than just stating there was a 'high risk of falls'.

---

### Not in the person's long term best interests

It is sometimes the case when assessing someone for DoLS that a placement does not appear to be in their best interests but there is no other alternative immediately available. This issue arose in the case of *A County Council v MB [2010] EWHC 2508*. The judge decided that in these circumstances, best interests assessors must consider what is immediately available and that a DoLS authorisation of limited duration may be the most suitable option. The duration chosen by the best interests assessor (and ultimately the authorising signatory on behalf of the local authority) then becomes important. This must be balanced against other situations such as in *North Yorkshire County Council v MAG & Ors [2015] EWCOP 64* where although there was no immediate alternative the judge refused to authorise a deprivation of liberty as the current placement was evidently not in the person's best interests (see page 57). Where best interests assessors consider this to be the case there is a specific part of the DoLS Form 3 to record this and a local authority would then need to take prompt action to rectify the situation.

---

### Taking risks

In the case of *A Local Authority X v MM & Anor [2007] EWHC 2003 (Fam)* the judge stated that best interests decisions should not simply aim to avoid all risks to the person concerned:

*"The fact is that all life involves risk, and the young, the elderly and the vulnerable, are exposed to additional risks and to risks they are less well equipped than others to cope with. But just as wise parents resist the temptation to keep their children metaphorically wrapped up in cotton wool, so too we must avoid the temptation always to put the physical health and safety of the elderly and the vulnerable before everything else ... The emphasis must be on sensible risk appraisal, not striving to avoid all risk, whatever the price, but instead seeking a proper balance and being willing to tolerate manageable or acceptable risks as the price appropriately to be paid in order to achieve some other*

*good – in particular to achieve the vital good of the elderly or vulnerable person's happiness. What good is it making someone safer if it merely makes them miserable?"*

This decision has been referenced (and quoted) in many other judgments. When making best interests decisions for another person under DoLS therefore a best interests assessor can suggest a course of action which involves risks for the person concerned. In some of these cases, given the risk or other factors, it may be appropriate to involve the Court of Protection.

In the case of *FP and GM v A Health Board [2011] EWHC 2778 (COP)* the judge weighed up the benefits and disadvantages for an older man between living at home with his daughter and grandson and remaining in a care home. The judge was heavily swayed by what he referred to as the *'emotional component'* and decided the man should be allowed to return to his own home despite the increased risk to his physical health in this setting. In explaining his reasoning he said:

*'On the one hand if the court goes down the line of authorising an admission to a care home, the court can be reasonably confident that all GM's physical and medical needs will be sufficiently and properly attended to.'* The judge noted that if the man returned to his own home the quality of physical care would be worse than in the care home but if he did return to his own home the following was true: *'...in the history of this case, such a placement contains a formidable emotional component which GM for over 20 years has clearly regarded as being of profound importance to him. These are the single most important relationships in his life. This is the place where he belongs, and where he matters in a sense that he could never matter in an institutional care setting.'*

There was medical evidence in the case that the man was perhaps only likely to live another year or two. The judge also felt this was an important consideration: *'I am very influenced by the desire to allow people where it is at all possible to spend their end time within the family rather than in an institution, even if there are shortcomings in terms of care which an institution could address'.*

---

**Practice points for assessors**

1. What evidence have you provided of your conversation or other attempts to find out the person's wishes and feelings? Have you highlighted when someone became emotional talking about a particular matter or perhaps, the person appeared to avoid a particular subject?
2. Have you explained why you gave weight to certain items in the best interests checklist compared to others?
3. Have you been careful not to discount wishes and feelings that are 'unreasonable' or challenge social norms?
4. Did you ask the person directly what they thought about the care home or hospital?
5. Could less restrictive options be tried for the person and what have you done to investigate this?
6. Do you think the person is distressed by their current situation?
7. Is your completed assessment an accurate and sensitive record of the person's and others expressed views? (Note: The person being assessed and their representative receive a full copy of all assessments).

---

**Frequently asked questions**

- *What if a person stated when they had capacity that they never wanted to go into a care home?*

If the person later lacks capacity, although their previous wishes would have to be considered, other relevant factors, such as the person's care needs would also need to be considered. A decision may still be lawfully taken to place them in a care home in their best interests.

- *Can a person demand a certain level of care?*

No. In the case *Aintree University Hospitals NHS Foundation Trust v James [2013] UKSC 67*, the Supreme Court stated: *'This Act is concerned with enabling the court to do for the patient what he could do for himself if of full capacity, but it goes no further. On an application under this Act therefore, the court has no greater powers than the patient would have if he were of full capacity.'*

- *Can a lasting power of attorney or a deputy authorise a deprivation of liberty and therefore, there would be no need for a DoLS authorisation?*

No. The Act allows a lasting power of attorney (or deputy) for personal welfare to object to the deprivation of liberty (no refusals assessment) but does not allow them to authorise one.

- *What about a person's next of kin, don't they make all the decisions?*

A 'next of kin' does not have any legal authority to make decisions on behalf of the person or authorise a deprivation of liberty. The term is not recognised under the Mental Capacity Act or DoLS. However any person interested in the welfare of the person should be consulted during the DoLS process as long as it is practicable and appropriate to do so.

- *I have assessed a person living at home who lacks capacity in relation to their care needs. They are in need of home adaptations in their best interests to them from coming to harm. Their partner has refused to have the adaptations installed?*

The partner should be informed that the Mental Capacity Act applies to your decision making and you are duty bound to act in the person's best interests which includes consulting with the partner. However, if the adaptations are in the best interests of the person lacking capacity and their health would deteriorate without them, you must take steps to safeguard the person lacking capacity. If it is the partner's property and they make it impossible for staff to access the person lacking capacity, then further legal advice should be sought and ultimately an application to the Court of Protection may be necessar.

- *What if making a best interests decision means making one based on what is in the best interests of the carers rather than the person who lacks capacity?*

The Mental Capacity Act (including DoLS) is clear that the decision must be based on the best interests of the person who lacks capacity. However there is a court case *(Re: Y (mental incapacity: bone marrow transplant) [1997] 2 FCR 172)* which adds context to this principle. In this case, the judge made a decision to allow the bone marrow transplant from 'Y' (who lacked capacity to consent to the procedure) to her sister, 'C' who had capacity (and needed the bone marrow). The decision was clearly not in Y's best medical interests as there was no clinical need for her to give the bone marrow, however other factors were relevant. The closest relationship Y had was with her mother. She appeared to gain a great deal from her mother's visits and showed her mother much affection. The judge was told that in the event of C's death, Y's mother would look after C's daughter; her only grandchild. The judge decided that there would be two consequences of the donation not going ahead. Firstly, the mother would spend less time with Y because of her new responsibilities looking after her granddaughter. Secondly, that any time she did spend with Y would deteriorate in quality due to the effects on her of losing C and looking after her six year old granddaughter. Neither of these consequences would be beneficial to Y so overall the judge ruled that the bone marrow transplant should go ahead in Y's best interests.

In DoLS cases, a BIA may consult with those caring for the person and establish that they will be unable to continue caring for the person at home without some respite care provision. It may be the person lacking capacity would prefer not to leave their home at all but on balance, it may be that short periods of respite would need to be organised in the person's best interests to ensure that the long term care at home is maintained. These periods of respite would need to be authorised under DoLS or possibly by the Court of Protection if they were a deprivation of liberty.

## Eligibility Assessment

The eligibility assessment considers whether the Mental Health Act 1983 or DoLS should be used according to a list of rules in the law and guidance from case law. It is undertaken by a mental health assessor who is also Section 12 approved or a best interests assessor who is also an AMHP. The person being assessed is only 'eligible' for DoLS in certain circumstances. This is the most technical area of DoLS as the interaction between the two forms of detention can be complex. In brief, the effects of the rules are:

---

**Hospital: no double detention**

In a hospital setting where a person is detained under a long term section of the Mental Health Act for the purpose of mental health treatment DoLS cannot be used as the person should not be subject to a 'double detention'. However, if the patient is compliant (see guidance below) and needs to be in hospital for mental health treatment, either DoLS or the MHA may be used.

---

**Community: care homes still need to apply for DoLS**

The provisions of the Mental Health Act that operate in the community (guardianship, community treatment orders, conditional discharge and section 17 leave) do not authorise a deprivation of liberty. DoLS can be used with all of these Mental Health Act community powers if the person's care plan in a care home means they are deprived of their liberty and they lack the mental capacity to consent to this.

---

**Gaps: rare cases may fall between the gaps in the eligibility rules**

Some people will fall into a legal gap between the Mental Health Act and DoLS. These cases will go to court and an order can be given under the inherent jurisdiction (see below).

| **Eligibility Assessment**<br>This assessment must be carried out by a mental health assessor who is also Section 12 approved or by a best interests assessor who is also an approved mental health professional (AMHP). | |
|---|---|
| **A person is NOT eligible for DoLS if they are:** | |
| **Detained**<br>Case A | Already detained in hospital (or another place registered to use the Act) under Section 2, 3, 4, 35, 36, 37, 38, 44, 45A, 47, 48 or 51 of the Mental Health Act 1983.<br><br>[Note: The Mental Capacity Act, including restraint, can be used to give physical treatment (unless that treatment is considered to be treatment for the mental disorder) to a person already detained under the Mental Health Act BUT a person cannot be detained under DoLS for physical treatment whilst also detained under the Mental Health Act 1983. If this is required seek legal advice]. |
| **On leave**<br>Case B | Subject to Section 2, 3, 4, 35, 36, 37, 38, 44, 45A, 47, 48 or 51 of MHA 1983 but not *currently* detained in hospital (on leave of absence)<br>**and**<br>the purpose of the (proposed) DoLS is to give treatment [wholly or partly] for mental disorder in hospital **or** the requirements of the DoLS would conflict with a requirement imposed on the person in connection with their leave under the MHA 1983 (for example, where they should live). |

| | |
|---|---|
| **Community Treatment Order (CTO)**<br>Case C | Subject to a community treatment order<br>**and**<br>the purpose of the (proposed) DoLS is to give treatment (wholly or partly) for mental disorder in hospital **or** the requirements of the DoLS would conflict with a requirement imposed on the person in connection with their CTO (for example, where they should live). |
| **Guardianship**<br>Case D | Subject to a guardianship order<br>**and**<br>the requirements of the DoLS would conflict with a requirement imposed on them in connection with their guardianship (for example, where they should live) **or** the purpose of the DoLS is to treat them for mental disorder in hospital<br>**and**<br>they object to either being in hospital as a mental health patient **or** they object to being given some or all of the treatment for their mental disorder [note: the wide definition of treatment in the Act]<br>**and**<br>an attorney or deputy, with the necessary authority, has not authorised it on their behalf (they lack capacity to the treatment) to the treatment. |
| **Could be detained under MHA 1983**<br>Case E | 1. Within the scope of the Mental Health Act (an application in respect of the person could be made under Section 2 or 3 of the Mental Health Act)<br>**and**<br>they could be detained in a hospital in pursuance of such an application, were one made. (Paragraph 12 Schedule 1A)<br>**and**<br>2. They **object** to either being in hospital as a mental health patient [in order to be given *mental health* treatment] **or** to being given some or all of the treatment for their *mental disorder [note: objecting? Regard to all the circumstances including: behaviour, wishes and feelings, views, beliefs and values - see below and the DoLS Code of Practice para 4.46-4.48]*<br>**and**<br>3. An attorney or deputy, with the necessary authority, has not consented on their behalf (they lack capacity to the treatment) to the treatment.<br><br>**Note:** If a person is NOT objecting to admission/treatment on a mental health ward (the compliant incapacitated patient) but the circumstances of their stay on a ward indicate they are being deprived of their liberty (eg. refusal to discharge the person) then *'...it will generally but not always be more appropriate to rely on DoLS in such circumstances...' '...a fact sensitive approach, ...in the search for and identification of the least restrictive way of best achieving the proposed assessment or treatment...'* should be undertaken.<br><br>*AM v SLAM & Secretary of State for Health [2013] UKUT 0365 (AAC)* |

### Objecting

The Code of Practice reminds eligibility assessors that it is not for them to decide on whether the objection (to being in hospital for treatment for their mental disorder) is reasonable or not. It is simply about whether the person has made an objection. For example, an objecting patient could be a patient who wants to return to a home that was sold ten years ago. The patient may not remember that it was sold but they are still expressing an objection. The law does not require the person to have the mental capacity to make the objection.

The DoLS Code of Practice (para 4.46) states: '*In many cases, the relevant person will be able to state an objection. However, where the person is unable to communicate, or can only communicate to a limited extent, assessors will need to consider the person's behaviour, wishes, feelings, views, beliefs and values, both present and past, so far as they can be ascertained...If there is reason to think that a person would object if able to do so, then the person should be assumed to be objecting. Occasionally, it may be that the person's behaviour initially suggests an objection, but that this objection is in fact not directed at the treatment at all. In that case, the person should not be taken to be objecting.'*

A patient might express an objection by saying things like 'I feel like I'm in prison!' or 'when can I go home?' or 'you've taken away my rights'. Some people may stay close to the door to try and physically leave. Alternatively, others may have been objecting but now they are so heavily medicated that they cannot object even if they wished to. This patient should still be taken to be an objecting patient.

The DoLS Code of Practice (para 4.47 and 4.48) notes: '*Assessors should always bear in mind that their job is simply to establish whether the person objects to treatment or to being in hospital: whether that objection is reasonable or not is not the issue...Even where a person does not object and a deprivation of liberty authorisation is possible, it should not be assumed that such an authorisation is invariably the correct course. There may be other factors that suggest the Mental Health Act 1983 should be used.'*

An example of the *other factors* referred to above is where a person is likely to recover mental capacity or has fluctuating capacity. The Mental Health Act would provide a more enduring authority to continue depriving the person of their liberty even if they regained mental capacity.

---

**Practical guidance**

In the case of *GJ v The Foundation Trust & Anor [2009] EWHC 2972 (Fam)*, the judge took the view that the meaning of *'could be detained under the Mental Health Act'* in case E above was to establish what the DoLS mental health assessor thought instead of the view of other clinicians. He said:

*'So, in my judgment the construction urged by the Secretary of State is the correct one, namely that the decision maker should approach paragraph 12(1) (a) and (b) by asking himself whether in his view the criteria set by, or the grounds in, s.2 or s.3 MHA 1983 are met (and if an application was made under them a hospital would detain P).'*

The Mental Health Act 1983 Code of Practice (para 13.60) warns:

*'The most pressing concern should always be that if an individual lacks capacity to consent to the matter in question and is deprived of their liberty they should receive the safeguards afforded under either the Act or through a DoLS authorisation or a Court of Protection order.'*

---

**Definition of treatment for mental disorder**

One of the eligibility requirements asks whether the person objects to treatment of their mental disorder. The Code of Practice to the Mental Health Act explains the definition of medical treatment for mental disorder as follows:

*'In the Act, 'medical treatment' includes nursing, psychological intervention and specialist mental health habilitation, rehabilitation and care. The Act defines medical treatment for mental disorder as medical treatment which is for the purpose of alleviating or preventing a worsening of a mental disorder or one or more of its symptoms or manifestations. This includes treatment of physical health problems only to the extent that such treatment is part of, or ancillary to, treatment for mental disorder (eg treating wounds self-inflicted as a result of mental disorder). Otherwise the Act does not regulate medical treatment for physical health problems.'*

---

**Case Law**

<u>Community treatment orders (CTO) and DoLS</u>

*PJ v A Local Health Board and Others [2015] UKUT 0480 (AAC)*
This case provides an example of a CTO's conditions resulting in a deprivation of liberty. The judge gave guidance to mental health tribunals that if the deprivation of liberty is not authorised, they can consider an adjournment to allow DoLS to be arranged but if that is not possible, they must discharge the CTO.

Section 17 and DoLS

*A Local Health Board v AB [2015] EWCOP 31*
In this case, the judge decided that the woman who was sent on Section 17 leave to the general hospital for physical treatment was not eligible for DoLS. The combined effect of her being on leave in a *hospital* with the wording of the eligibility rules meant DoLS could not be applied. Instead the court authorised the surgery and the deprivation of liberty under its inherent jurisdiction as deprivation of liberty under the Mental Capacity Act was not possible.

Guardianship and DoLS

*NM v Kent County Council (2015) UKUT 125 (AAC)*
In this case, the local authority challenged the need for both guardianship and DoLS. They argued that DoLS alone was sufficient to appropriately care and supervise the person concerned. However, the court found some distinct reasons why in this particular case, it was preferable to have both in place. This included the power to return the person under guardianship if he absconded from the care home. In the circumstances of other cases, the court accepted that there may be no need to use both and DoLS would provide sufficient protection in a care home.

*KD v A Borough Council, the Department of Health and Others [2015] UKUT 251 (AAC)*
In this case, it was again accepted that a deprivation of liberty while a person was under guardianship would need to be authorised under DoLS. The judge provided guidance for the professionals involved: '*A deprivation of liberty during guardianship can and so should be authorised under the MCA (and so here its DOLS). Accordingly, it would be prudent for a Guardian and the managing authority and supervisory body of the relevant care home to consider whether a DOLS authorisation should be obtained in respect of a placement of P in a care home required by a Guardian when P's care plan there creates or may create a deprivation of P's liberty.*'

Conditional discharge and DoLS

*Secretary of State for Justice v KC and C Partnership NHS Foundation Trust [2015] UKUT 376 (AAC)*
In this case, the judge confirmed that a DoLS authorisation could be granted for someone who was to be subject to a conditional discharge if the conditions imposed on them would amount to a deprivation of liberty. If the person was not to reside in a care home, the Court of Protection would be able to grant an order to authorise the deprivation of liberty instead. The judge summarised: '*The FTT* [First Tier Tribunal] *has power to impose (and so direct a conditional discharge on) conditions that when implemented will, on an objective assessment, give rise to a deprivation of liberty that is lawful because it has been authorised by the Court of Protection under the MCA or pursuant to the DoLS contained in the MCA (the MCA authorisations) and so complies with Article 5.*'

In this situation DoLS assessors and the court would not be able to override the conditions imposed by the first tier tribunal therefore limiting the scope of investigating less restrictive options.

---

**Frequently asked questions**

- *Can the Court of Protection override a guardian under the Mental Health Act?*

No. In the case of *C v Blackburn and Darwen Borough Council [2011] EWHC 3321 (COP)* the judge decided that the Court of Protection could not override the guardian's powers. In the recent case of *KD v A Borough Council, the Department of Health and Others [2015] UKUT 251 (AAC),* the judge agreed.

- *I thought a person was still detained if they were on Section 17 leave?*

No. The person is *liable to be detained* which is different to actually currently being detained in hospital under a detaining section. So, they could go on leave to a care home which might be a trial before they are discharged. The care home staff could then use DoLS to then authorise a deprivation of liberty in the care home.

- *Doesn't the Mental Health Act 1983 have primacy over the use of DoLS?*

No. The judge that said this in relation to Case E above in *GJ v The Foundation Trust & Anor [2009] EWHC 2972 (Fam)* effectively retracted this statement in the case of *AM v SLAM & Secretary of State for Health [2013] UKUT 0365 (AAC).* He said that in fact, depending on the circumstances: '*...the regimes provide relevant and available alternatives.'*

The decision as to which Act should be used must be made on the basis of which option will be less restrictive for the person involved. Considerations such as stigma of detention under the Mental Health Act and the possibility of adding conditions (from the outset) to the DoLS to allow access to the community could make DoLS less restrictive. However, the judge made it clear that DoLS will not *always* be less restrictive. A view echoed in the Mental Health Act Code of Practice (para 13.59):

*'Both regimes provide appropriate procedural safeguards to ensure the rights of the person concerned are protected during the detention. Decision-makers should not therefore proceed on the basis that one regime generally provides greater safeguards than the other. However, the nature of the safeguards provided under the two regimes are different and decision-makers will wish to exercise their professional judgement in determining which safeguards are more likely to best protect the interests of the patient in the particular circumstances of each individual case.'*

Please note: the eligibility assessment does not require the assessor to check whether the Mental Health Act or DoLS is the less restrictive option. They simply need to say whether the person is eligible.

- *What if a person is just wandering in general and happens to go the main ward exit door, is this objecting?*

Not necessarily. Staff must make a judgement whether the person is purposely going towards the exit door or simply wandering around the ward and at times this happens to be the near the exit door.

- *What is the inherent jurisdiction?*

In the context of this area of law, the inherent jurisdiction is the power of the High Court to make decisions for people who lack capacity (due to mental incapacity or incapacity caused by coercion) when a person's case falls into a gap between Acts of Parliament such as the Mental Health Act 1983 or Mental Capacity Act 2005. This was explained in the case of *XCC v AA [2012] EWHC 2183 (COP):*

*'The protection or intervention of the inherent jurisdiction of the High Court is available to those lacking capacity within the meaning of the MCA 2005 as it is to capacitous but vulnerable adults who have had their will overborne, and on the same basis, where the remedy sought does not fall within the repertoire of remedies provided for in the MCA 2005.'*

The inherent jurisdiction was used in the case of *A NHS Trust v Dr A [2013] EWHC 2442 (COP).* In this case a man known as Dr A was detained under the Mental Health Act for the purpose of his mental disorder but the treatment the trust wanted to impose on him was considered to be treatment of his physical health which could not given under the Mental Health Act. However, the treatment (force feeding with restraint including sedation) would have resulted in a deprivation of liberty. As he was already detained under the Mental Health Act (case A above) he could not be 'double detained' under DoLS as well. The Court of Protection used its powers under the inherent jurisdiction. The judge stated: *'In all the circumstances, I hold that this court has the power under its inherent jurisdiction to make a declaration and order authorising the treatment of an incapacitated adult that includes the provision for the deprivation of his liberty provided that the order complies with Article 5...it will therefore be necessary, in any case in which a hospital wishes to give treatment to a patient who is ineligible under section 16A, for the hospital to apply for an order under the inherent jurisdiction where the treatment (a) is outside the meaning of medical treatment of the MHA 1983 and (b) involves the deprivation of a patient's liberty.'*

## Equivalent Assessments

DoLS allows for the use of what are called *equivalent* assessments (Paragraph 49 Schedule A1). This is where a person already has an assessment on file that meets the criteria below allowing it to be used as one of the assessments for a standard authorisation.

a) it meets the DoLS criteria
b) a written copy is in the possession of the local authority
c) there is no reason to believe it is not accurate
d) it was completed within the last 12 months (not necessarily for DoLS)

The only exception to this is the age assessment which does not have the 12 month limitation (if the person has already been found to be at least 18 once, they clearly will not get any younger).

In addition to points a) to d) above, if the assessment is a best interests assessment, the local authority must also take account of any information given by the representative or an IMCA (appointed under Sections 39C or D).

The DoLS Code of Practice (para 4.6) notes: *'Great care should be taken in deciding to use an equivalent assessment and this should not be done routinely. The older the assessment is, even if it took place within the last 12 months, the less likely it is to represent a valid equivalent assessment (unless it is an age assessment). For example, only a very recent mental capacity assessment would be appropriate where capacity is known to fluctuate...'* The Code also states that local authorities should record their reasons for using an equivalent assessment.

## Duration

The local authority sets the duration of a standard DoLS authorisation (DoLS Form 5). The period set can last up to 12 months but cannot be longer than that recommended by the best interests assessor in their assessment. The DoLS Code of Practice (para 4.71) notes: '*The underlying principle is that deprivation of liberty should be for the minimum period necessary so, for the maximum 12-month period to apply, the assessor will need to be confident that there is unlikely to be a change in the person's circumstances that would affect the authorisation within that timescale'.*

---

### Procedure

As part of their assessment a BIA is required to recommend a maximum time period for a standard authorisation. The DoLS Code of Practice (para 4.71) notes: *'The assessor should set out the reasons for selecting the period stated. This decision will be based on the information obtained during the consultation process...'* The Code further states the decision about duration should be based on the:

- history of the resident
- prognosis / expected progression of their illness
- potential effect of treatment

Providing a clear rationale for deciding the duration is important as this element of DoLS can be challenged in the Court of Protection. If a person has a fixed condition which means the restrictions necessitating the use of DoLS are very unlikely to change and any treatment given is unlikely to make any difference then it could be expected that a longer term duration up to 12 months is recommended by the BIA. The exception to this might be if the placement itself is not appropriate (see case law below). It is however for the BIA themselves to decide an appropriate period of time. Although the BIA *recommends* the maximum duration, it is the local authority through the authorising signatory that decides on the actual duration of the standard DoLS authorisation. This cannot be any longer than that recommended by the BIA but the authorising signatory can reduce the duration if they think it appropriate.

---

### Case law on duration

Recent case law *(P v Surrey CC & Surrey Downs CCG [2015] EWCOP 54)* has considered the duration given to a standard authorsation. In this case three separate people including the BIA noted concerns about the current placement for an individual being assessed for DoLS. The BIA in their assessment wrote a standard authorisation should be *'in the short term'* and was needed for a *'short period of time'*. They then recommended a duration of 12 months and the authorising signatory, on behalf of the local authority, granted the standard authorisation with the duration reduced to ten months. Although the local authority had reduced the duration the judge was critical of the local authority's decision to set it at ten months:

*'What was, in my judgment, not open to the supervisory body was to do what it did, namely to receive un-contradicted information from three separate sources that the care home was only suitable in the short term or for a short period and then proceed to grant the standard authorisation for a substantial period.'*

---

### Delayed duration

A standard authorisation can come into force at a time after it is granted (Paragraph 63(2) Schedule A1). This could be used, for example, if a person was in a care home but was due to be admitted to hospital for surgery where they would need to be deprived of their liberty during their stay. A standard authorisation could be given but its start delayed until the person was actually admitted to the hospital.

## Conditions

A standard authorisation may have conditions attached to it (Paragraph 53 Schedule A1) with the aim of reducing restrictions in a care plan. The Act does not define what these conditions could be but an example may be ensuring the person goes out with an escort every day for half an hour. The local authority is responsible for deciding what, if any, conditions are attached to a standard authorisation and the care home or hospital is then responsible for ensuring they are fulfilled. The positive impact of conditions has been noted by health and social care inspectors[8]: *'Inspectors did see a number of very good examples where conditions had been used to great effect to protect an individual's human rights and improve their outcomes.'*

---

### Procedure

As part of their assessment for a standard authorisation, best interests assessors are able to recommend conditions be attached to the authorisation (Paragraph 43 Schedule A1). The DoLS Code of Practice (para 4.75) states: *'It would be good practice for the best interests assessor to discuss any proposed conditions with the relevant personnel at the home or hospital before finalising the assessment ...'*

Although a BIA may recommend that certain conditions are attached to a standard authorisation, it is the local authority through the authorisation process that decides on the actual conditions. The local authority must *have regard* to any recommendations in the best interests assessment about such conditions. The local authority can then decide whether to agree to the conditions, remove one or more or add other conditions not suggested by the BIA. If the local authority does not intend to agree to the conditions suggested by the BIA it should consult them as this may affect the BIA's overall view in relation to whether deprivation is in the person's best interests. Indeed, if a BIA does recommend conditions in their assessment for DoLS they should record whether any changes to them made by the local authority would significantly affect the other judgments they have reached.

---

### Purpose of conditions

The DoLS Code of Practice (para 4.74) provides some examples of possible conditions: *'For example, they may make recommendations around contact issues, issues relevant to the person's culture or other major issues related to the deprivation of liberty, which – if not dealt with – would mean that the deprivation of liberty would cease to be in the person's best interests. The best interests assessor may also recommend conditions in order to work towards avoiding deprivation of liberty in future. But it is not the best interests assessor's role to specify conditions that do not directly relate to the issue of deprivation of liberty.'*

It is not lawful to use conditions to restrict contact with family or other people the individual is close to. Such actions are an interference of Article 8: ECHR, the right to respect for private and family life and require authority from the Court of Protection.

The DoLS Code of Practice (para 4.75) also notes: *'In recommending conditions, best interests assessors should aim to impose the minimum necessary constraints so that they do not unnecessarily prevent or inhibit the staff of the hospital or care home from responding appropriately to the person's needs, whether they remain the same or vary over time.'*

---

### Authority of conditions

The DoLS legislation states: *'... the relevant hospital or care home must ensure that any conditions are complied with'* (Paragraph 53 Schedule A1). Care home or hospital staff therefore should ensure any conditions attached to a DoLS authorisation are incorporated into regular care planning. Care homes and hospitals should monitor whether stated conditions are being met in practice. If they are not the local authority should be informed and a review requested. Although local authorities are not able to directly enforce compliance with conditions under the Act (for example by way of sanctions) failure to meet stated conditions can be challenged in the Court of Protection (see page 84). It may be appropriate for the local authority to have an internal process by which they can monitor compliance with conditions.

**Practical advice**

If a local authority attaches conditions to a standard authorisation it is important they are clearly written so that the care home or hospital understands what is required. One way of doing this is for local authorities to ensure conditions are written in the SMART format. This is not a legal requirement but may assist in practice.

| | |
|---|---|
| **S**pecific | unambiguous and clear to the staff of a care home or hospital |
| **M**easurable | the care home or hospital and local authority should be given a means of gauging/evaluating whether the conditions are being met |
| **A**chievable | any condition set must be something that the care home or hospital can reasonably achieve |
| **R**elevant | the condition must be directly related to the purpose or reason for the DoLS |
| **T**ime specific | this should detail when the condition should be accomplished or state that it is an ongoing requirement |

For example, a BIA may feel a person under DoLS needs their medication reviewed. A condition could be that a care home, within two weeks of the DoLS starting, makes a referral to the local GP for a medication review. However a condition that stated a care home had to review and change the medication in two weeks would be inappropriate because this is outside their control.

Other examples could include a weekly visit to their place of worship or visits to a recreational activity they used to participate in before.

## The Representative (RPR)

Every person under a standard DoLS authorisation must have an independent representative appointed for them (formally called the relevant person's representative (RPR)). This person is appointed by the local authority when a standard DoLS is granted or as soon as possible afterwards. Representatives can be a relative or friend of the person deprived of their liberty. If a person has no friends or family suitable to be appointed, a professional independent paid representative is appointed.

---

### Role of the representative

The purpose of the representative is to ensure the person under DoLS has someone to support them in matters relating to the authorisation, for example, by asking for a review of the standard authorisation or challenging the DoLS authorisation in the Court of Protection.

---

### Selection of representatives

The DoLS Code of Practice advises that the process of identifying the representative should begin as soon as the assessment process for a standard DoLS authorisation begins. It is the role of the BIA to identify an appropriate representative during their assessment for the standard authorisation. They are then formally appointed by the local authority. A representative must be at least 18 years old and willing to be appointed. Only one representative can be appointed under the Act. Even if two people want to take on the role and qualify only one can legally be appointed by a local authority.

Relatives who are opposed to the DoLS authorisation can be representatives, the DoLS Code of Practice (para 7.17) notes: *'It should not be assumed that the representative needs to be someone who supports the deprivation of liberty.'*

The Act states (Paragraph 140 Schedule A1) that the appointment of a person as a representative:

> *'... must not be made unless it appears to the person making the selection that the prospective representative would, if appointed:*
>
> *(a) maintain contact with the relevant person,*
>
> *(b) represent the relevant person in matters relating to or connected with this Schedule, and*
>
> *(c) support the relevant person in matters relating to or connected with this Schedule.'*

The importance of this part of the Act was identified by the Court of Protection *(AJ v A Local Authority [2015] EWCOP 5)* where the judge stated: *'... Paragraph 140, which is a statutory provision, is in mandatory terms. The selection must not be made unless it appears to the person making it that the prospective RPR would maintain contact with P and would represent and support P in matters relating to the Schedule.'* He continued: *'... "matters relating to or connected with this Schedule" must to my mind include, inter alia, challenging any authorisation granted under the Schedule.'* It should be noted, this means appealing to the Court of Protection rather than just requesting a review of the DoLS by the local authority.

In the case of AJ above, the representative was a relative and despite clear objections from AJ to being placed in a care home, they did not appeal to the Court of Protection on her behalf. The judge, Mr Justice Baker, concluded: *'... it is likely to be difficult for a close relative or friend who believes that it is in P's best interests to move into residential care, and has been actively involved in arranging such a move, into a placement that involves a deprivation of liberty, to fulfil the functions of RPR, which involve making a challenge to any authorisation of that deprivation. BIAs and local authorities should therefore scrutinise very carefully the selection and appointment of RPRs in circumstances which are likely to give rise to this potential conflict of interest.'*

This does not mean relatives or friends cannot be chosen to be representatives, however the BIA must talk to them about the requirements of the role. This includes whether they would challenge the DoLS authorisation if the person needed their support to do so or, if it was appropriate, challenge for another reason. BIAs may want to consider asking the representative how they would respond if they thought a care plan was becoming too restrictive or if the person under DoLS said they wanted to go home. If the proposed representative is against the idea of going to court in these circumstances either because they do not feel it is in the person's best interests or they consider going to court daunting, they may not be appropriate. However this may be overcome by appointing an IMCA (advocate) to support them in the role.

In relation to the duty on representatives to maintain contact with the person under DoLS, the legislation does not define either the nature or frequency of the contact required. The DoLS Code of Practice however states that face-to-face contact is required (para 7.25).

The duties of local authorities in relation to monitoring the role of representatives are discussed further on page 93.

The appointment of a representative is separate to, and in addition to, the appointment of attorneys, deputies and nearest relatives (under the Mental Health Act 1983). All these people have their own roles and corresponding duties even if they also choose to take on the role of representative with its additional responsibilities.

---

**Conflicts of interest**

Statutory regulation No. 1315 (The Mental Capacity (Deprivation of Liberty: Appointment of Relevant Person's Representative) Regulations 2008) states a person cannot be a representative if they are:

- financially interested in the relevant person's care home or hospital (see page 125)
- a relative of a person who is financially interested in the care home or hospital (see page 125 for definition of relative)
- employed by, or providing services to, the relevant person's care home
- employed to work in the relevant person's hospital in a role that is, or could be, related to the relevant person's case
- employed by the local authority.

---

**Procedure for appointment**

The procedure for identifying and appointing a representative follows a hierarchy:

1. If the person being assessed for an authorisation is judged to have capacity to choose a representative they may do so. They can choose a family member, friend or carer. Under the statutory regulations, this requires the BIA to assess if the person has capacity to make this decision (see page 47 on assessing capacity). An important point to consider will be what information a person needs to understand in relation to choosing a representative. The legislation and Code of Practice do not consider this. As a general rule however (MCA Code of Practice, paragraph 4.16) when considering what information a person needs to understand in relation to a particular decision, it should encompass the <u>nature</u> of what is going to happen (in this case, appointment of a person to be a representative for them) the <u>purpose</u> of it (what a representative does such as maintain contact, support or ask for a review or appeal to the Court of Protection) and the <u>consequences</u> of making a decision or not (a person they name will become their representative otherwise someone else will make the choice on their behalf, see below). If a person has capacity to make a choice the BIA has to confirm that the person chosen is eligible in accordance with the regulations described above. It would be advisable for local authorities to clarify with BIAs what information a person needs to understand for this decision. Give the nature of this decision the minimum information a person needs to understand should be the same regardless of who the BIA is or who they are assessing.

2. If the person lacks capacity to choose a representative then any attorney or deputy (with relevant authority) can nominate one. The attorney or deputy can also nominate themselves providing they meet the requirements listed above. The best interests assessor has to confirm that the person chosen by an attorney or deputy is eligible in accordance with the regulations described above. If the person selected by them is not eligible, the best interests assessor must advise the attorney or deputy who has made the choice and ask them to make another selection.

3. If the person, their attorney or deputy cannot or will not select someone, a representative would then be selected by the best interests assessor. However, the best interests assessor cannot select someone the person being assessed for DoLS, their attorney or deputy objects to. If the BIA cannot

select someone (because either the relevant person objects or no one fits the criteria in the regulations), they must notify the local authority.

4. If the BIA is unable to identify a representative, the local authority must select someone. However, unlike a best interests assessor, when a local authority selects a representative they cannot choose a family member, friend or carer of the person. The person they choose must perform the role in a professional capacity and have satisfactory skills and experience. This could, for example, be an IMCA (advocate) paid to act as a representative or any other person the local authority considers suitable. The local authority must also ensure that they have obtained a DBS check for the person.

In all of the cases listed above (1-3) it remains at the discretion of the local authority to appoint an identified person as the representative. Even if a person has been identified and put forward by a BIA the local authority can still decide not to appoint them if they do not consider they meet the requirements of the legislation.

The local authority must formally appoint the selected representative in writing giving information about the role, duties and duration of appointment. The representative must confirm in writing they accept the appointment and that they have understood the duties involved. If the representative refuses, the process of selection and appointment must continue until a representative is appointed. Copies of the appointment (and any later terminations of that appointment) must be sent to:

- the representative
- the person under DoLS
- any deputies or attorneys
- the care home or hospital concerned
- any IMCA involved (even if not appointed specifically in relation to the authorisation)
- every interested person named by the best interests assessor in their report as someone they have consulted in carrying out the assessment.

---

**Changes of representative**

A representative's appointment will end if the representative dies, or informs the local authority that they no longer wish to continue, or the period of their appointment ends (for example, when the standard authorisation ends). It will also end if the person, or an attorney or deputy who originally selected the representative, now objects to the appointment. The local authority can also remove a representative if they believe they are not acting in the person's best interests, are not eligible or are not keeping in sufficient contact with the person under DoLS. Local authorities can use DoLS Form 8 (see page 126) to record changes in representatives.

At any point during a standard authorisation when there is no acting representative (for whatever reason) the local authority must assign an advocate (IMCA) for the person concerned until a new representative is identified and appointed.

---

**Contact**

In order to carry out their role effectively, the DoLS Code of Practice states that care homes and hospitals should ensure they accommodate visits by representatives at reasonable times and (para 7.27): *'When the managing authority is reviewing the person's care plan, it should consider whether the representative is in sufficient contact with the relevant person to offer effective support. Records kept by managing authorities about the frequency of contact will support this consideration.'*

Neither the legislation nor the Code of Practice states what an appropriate frequency of contact is so care homes and hospitals will need to use their own judgement. Care homes and hospitals are advised by the Code to raise the issue of insufficient contact with the representative in the first instance. If this does not resolve the situation, they should contact the local authority. The DoLS Code of Practice does state (paragraph 7.25) that contact should be face-to-face.

**IMCA and information on rights**

There is a right to free independent advocacy support (IMCA) for all representatives at any time. This is discussed in the following chapter. In addition, care homes or hospitals must provide both the person under DoLS and their representative with relevant information about their rights. The DoLS Code of Practice (para 7.5) advises: *'...the managing authority should take account of the communication and language needs of both the person and their representative. Provision of information should be seen as an ongoing responsibility, rather than a one-off activity.'*

---

**Appeals to the Court of Protection**

In the case of *AJ v A Local Authority [2015] EWCOP 5,* the Court of Protection highlighted the key function of a representative was to appeal on behalf of the person under DoLS if they were objecting (which could be verbal or physical). The exact nature or frequency of objections that would necessitate an 'appeal' under DoLS was not examined in the case as the woman involved clearly and repeatedly stated she wanted to leave. If however a person says they want to leave a care home or hospital (despite the fact they have nowhere else to go to) or they physically indicate they want to leave this as a minimum should be taken as a wish to appeal the DoLS in the Court of Protection. The role of the representative is to support or enable the person to make that appeal.

At present the form required by the Court of Protection (Form COPDLA) for a representative to appeal is detailed and in order to support a successful application some local authorities are providing an advocate (IMCA) or other person to help representatives with the form.

---

**Involvement of representatives**

Representatives have a duty to support and represent the person in relation to the DoLS. Care homes and hospitals should inform them of key decisions about the care of the person concerned. The representative does not replace the role of relatives or others but they must be informed of care planning decisions because changes may mean they need to consider whether a DoLS review or appeal is necessary.

---

**Concerns about representatives**

If a care home or hospital is concerned about the actions of a representative they should contact the DoLS office of the local authority responsible.

# Advocacy (IMCA)

DoLS provides a statutory right to advocacy (Part 11 of Schedule A1 and Sections 39A-D of the Act) for people being assessed for, or subject to DoLS. Independent mental capacity advocates (IMCAs) are independent of health and social services and their role is defined within the legislation. Every local authority is responsible for commissioning independent groups (usually charities or non-profit organisations) to provide a local IMCA service to meet the requirements of the Act. Local authorities have a legal duty to make referrals to the IMCA service for some people under DoLS.

Health and social care inspectors in Wales have voiced concern[8] about the lack of IMCA referrals: *'The number of referrals to Independent Mental Capacity Advocates (IMCA) was very low overall across Wales. The role of the IMCA in supporting and representing the Relevant Person and their representative through the complex decision-making process is vital, but was not actively promoted by some Supervisory Bodies.'*

---

### Appointment of an IMCA

There are a number of different ways in which an IMCA can be appointed under DoLS. The manner in which they are appointed has an impact on their responsibilities and the duties of other bodies towards them. The local authority **must** appoint an IMCA when:

1. There is no one appropriate to consult when undertaking the assessment of the person's best interests for the purposes of a DoLS authorisation. (Section 39A)
2. An assessor has been appointed to determine whether there has been an unauthorised deprivation of liberty and there is no one appropriate to consult in determining the person's best interests (friend or carer or relative etc but not someone who is engaged in providing care or treatment to the person) (Section 39A)
3. There are gaps in appointing a representative for a person under DoLS. (Section 39C)
4. The person or their representative (if they are not a paid professional) requests an IMCA. (Section 39D)
5. the local authority have reason to believe one or more of the following:
   (a) without the help of an advocate, the person under DoLS or their representative (unpaid) would be unable to exercise one or more of the relevant rights (Section 39D)
   (b) the person under DoLS or their representative (unpaid) have each failed to exercise a relevant right when it would have been reasonable to exercise it (Section 39D)
   (c) the person under DoLS or their representative (unpaid) are each unlikely to exercise a relevant right when it would be reasonable to exercise it. (Section 39D)

In relation to point 5 above, the Court of Protection *(AJ v A Local Authority [2015] EWCOP 5)* has stated: *'... an IMCA appointed under Section 39D must act with diligence and urgency to ensure that any challenge to an authorisation under Schedule A1 is brought before the court expeditiously. Failure to do so will lead to the evaporation of P's Article 5 rights.'*

---

### Comment

There has been repeated concern since DoLS began that some local authorities are failing to appoint advocates under Section 39D above when it would appear appropriate to do so. An argument, supported by the courts, is that very few people lacking capacity under DoLS or their representatives (if unpaid family or carers) would be able to exercise their rights without the support of an IMCA given the complexity of the legislation and therefore local authorities should be proactive in appointing IMCAs under Section 39D. The Department of Health in its last annual report on IMCA provision[18] stated: *'All local authorities should review their processes and procedures for providing 39D IMCA support to unpaid representatives to ensure that the right people are given access to this valuable service ... it's important that they are provided with support to enable them to understand DoLS and also to challenge when necessary.'*

Any delay in appointing an advocate can mean that their ability to act effectively for the person is diminished. For example, there have been a number of cases where IMCAs have applied to the Court of Protection to prevent the sale of a home, to allow for further investigation of whether a person could return to their own home as a less restrictive option. If local authorities delay the appointment it may be too late to take such action thus limiting the scope for considering less restrictive options.

---

**IMCA role**

The role of IMCAs for people under DoLS includes:

- Support to help the person under DoLS and their representative understand their rights, and the reasons for and effects of, an authorisation given under DOLS.
- Support with requesting a review or exercising other rights.
- Applying to the Court of Protection for permission to take the person's case to court. Alternatively, the IMCA may provide support to the person or their representative if they wish to make an application to the court themselves.

The role of an IMCA appointed under Section 39D is extensive and the legislation states (P is the person under DoLS and R is the representative):

*'If an advocate is appointed under this section, the advocate is, in particular, to take such steps as are practicable to help P and R to understand the following matters —*

*(a) the effect of the authorisation;*
*(b) the purpose of the authorisation;*
*(c) the duration of the authorisation;*
*(d) any conditions to which the authorisation is subject;*
*(e) the reasons why each assessor who carried out an assessment in connection with the request for the authorisation, or in connection with a review of the authorisation, decided that P met the qualifying requirement in question;*
*(f) the relevant rights;*
*(g) how to exercise the relevant rights.*

*(8) The advocate is, in particular, to take such steps as are practicable to help P or R —*
*(a) to exercise the right to apply to court, if it appears to the advocate that P or R wishes to exercise that right, or*
*(b) to exercise the right of review, if it appears to the advocate that P or R wishes to exercise that right.'*

The Court of Protection addressed the role of Section 39D advocates in the case of *AJ v A Local Authority [2015] EWCOP 5.* One of the key findings by the judge in this case was that the role of a 39D advocate, based on the legislation stated above, was not to determine the best interests of the person concerned but rather it was to help the person or their representative understand their rights and to support them in exercising those rights. In this case when the person objected to the placement, the IMCA should have taken this as a wish to appeal and they should have applied to the court on the person's behalf. If a person is objecting to their placement and neither the representative or IMCA appeals for them, there is little point in the safeguards being available. They have to be real and effective safeguards if they are to have any value.

---

**IMCA authority**

IMCAs appointed during the assessment process of DoLS have a number of legal powers and local authorities have certain legal duties towards them (these duties vary according to which provision the IMCA is appointed under):

- give information to the DoLS assessors which must be taken into account
- receive copies of assessments and DoLS authorisations
- be notified of any failed assessments

- be notified when urgent authorisations granted, extended or ended
- be notified when requests to extend urgent authorisations are granted or refused
- be notified when a suspension of a standard authorisation is lifted
- be notified when a review of a standard authorisation has been completed and the outcome

---

**Concerns about IMCAs**

The CQC has voiced some concern about how proactive IMCAs are in relation to DoLS[10]: *'There appears to be variation in practice among IMCAs in how actively they encourage people subject to authorisation and their representatives to ask for reviews or to challenge the authorisation to the Court of Protection. We encourage IMCAs to share knowledge of how and when to do this, and IMCA organisations to support their staff to gain the knowledge and confidence to help people affected by the Deprivation of Liberty Safeguards to challenge the status quo.'*

---

**Case law example**

An example of an IMCA supporting a person to appeal against a standard authorisation is found in the case of *Re: M [2013] EWHC 3456 (COP)*. In this case a woman, who had been deprived of her liberty in a care home because of concerns about her ability to cope at home by her local NHS Clinical Commissioning Group (CCG), stated she wanted to return to live in her own home. With the support of an IMCA she was able to appeal to the Court of Protection which subsequently discharged the DoLS so that she could return home.

In another deprivation of liberty case, *London Borough of Hillingdon v Neary & Anor [2011] EWCOP 1377* an IMCA's report was commended by the judge: *'On 18 November, the IMCA delivered her report. It is an impressive document. For the first time, professional support was given to Mr Neary's arguments. The previous best interests assessments are subjected to analysis. The IMCA's conclusion is that Hillingdon was potentially not acting in Steven's best interests by refusing his father's request to have his son live with him at home. The fact that this is the most important relationship in Steven's life was noted'.* Later, the judge stated: *'The first best interests assessment that deserves the name is the IMCA report of 18 November 2010.'*

# Reviews

A standard authorisation can be reviewed at any time (reviews do not apply to urgent authorisations). Reviews are carried out by the local authority. In order to undertake a review, the DoLS assessors (on the instruction of the local authority) undertake some or all of the original assessments. These are not neccessarily the same assessors as undertook the original assessments but they may be. A review will result in either the authorisation continuing or being ended by the local authority or the conditions attached being changed, deleted or new conditions added.

The latest statistics for England[2] show there were just under 2,000 reviews of authorisations completed during the year ending March 2015. The rate of reviews shows marked regional variation with 8% of authorisations being reviewed in the West Midlands whilst only 1% were reviewed in Yorkshire and the Humber. Statistics on the outcome of the reviews are given overleaf.

---

Paragraph 102 Schedule A1 states a local authority may carry out a review at any time but they **must** do so when either the person under DoLS, their representative (or the 39C IMCA if no representative at present) or the care home or hospital requests one. There is a standard form available for this (DoLS Form 10 see page 126) but it is not a statutory form and the request for a review can be made in any manner, including for example a verbal request.

The grounds for a review being carried out are:

- There is a change in the person's situation and therefore an existing condition should be amended, a new condition added or an old condition removed.
- The reasons the person meets the qualifying requirements (any of the six assessments) are different from the reasons originally stated in the standard authorisation. In this situation, the care home or hospital must request a review.
- The person no longer meets one or more of the qualifying requirements (the six assessments). In this situation the care home or hospital must request a review.
- The person is no longer eligible because they now object to receiving mental health treatment or being in hospital for mental health treatment. Note: If they are not eligible for any other reason, the DoLS authorisation must be suspended (see page 88)

The DoLS Code of Practice (para 8.9 and 8.10) notes: '*When a supervisory body receives a request for a review, it must first decide which, if any, of the qualifying requirements need to be reviewed ... If the supervisory body concludes that none of the qualifying requirements need to be reviewed no further action is necessary.*'

---

**Informing others**

The person under DoLS, their representative (or 39C IMCA if no representative at present) and the care home or hospital must be informed by the local authority (Paragraphs 108 and 120 Schedule A1) when a review is to be undertaken and also when the outcome is known. If an IMCA is involved (39D) the local authority has to inform them of the outcome of a review. Local authorities must keep a record of all requests for reviews and their outcomes (Paragraph 121 Schedule A1).

---

**Review assessments**

Only those criteria (the original six assessments) that are being questioned need to be reviewed. For example, if only the mental health assessment is reviewable, only that one would be reassessed and not the other five.

The best interests assessment does not need to be reviewed if the reason for the review is to change the existing conditions and the change in the person's case is not significant. When deciding whether a change is significant or not, the nature and duration of the change should be considered (Paragraph 111 Schedule A1). It is important therefore that evidence of any change is included in the review request. The assessments are known as review assessments, for example, 'a mental capacity *review* assessment'. The standard authorisation will be terminated if any of the reviews result in a failed assessment (the person no longer meets one of the DoLS criteria). The Act does not state how often a review can be requested.

If a care home or hospital requests a further standard DoLS authorisation, a review cannot be requested while the assessment process for the new standard authorisation is being undertaken. If a review has already begun and a care home or hospital then requests a further standard authorisation, the review must stop until a decision is reached on whether to grant a new authorisation (Paragraph 123 Schedule A1). In addition if a DoLS authorisation is suspended (see page 88) a review cannot be carried out. If a review is underway before the DoLS is suspended, the review must stop as long as the DoLS remains suspended (Paragraph 122 Schedule A1).

---

### Authority of reviews

Although a review can end or discharge a DoLS, the CQC has noted[10]: *'A review under the Safeguards is not a substitute for the requirement under the Human Rights Act 1998 Article 5(4) that a detained person must have speedy access to a court, which has the power to discharge the detention, to challenge it – the supervisory body which carries out reviews does of course have the power to lift an authorisation but it is not independent or judicial.'*

---

### Role of IMCA

If an IMCA helps a person under DoLS or their representative to request a review, the advocate (Section 39D) has the statutory right to make submissions to the local authority on the question of whether a qualifying requirement is reviewable and the advocate may give information, or make submissions, to any assessor carrying out a review assessment.

---

### Commentary

The CQC in its annual DoLS[10] report found: *'Fewer than 10% of the reviews were done as a result of a request from the relevant person, their representative, or an IMCA. This is a low proportion, and while reasons for it undoubtedly vary, it would be good practice, particularly for longer periods of authorisation, for a supervisory body to decide to carry out a review if they think it might be necessary and to be assured that it is easy for the person subject to authorisation (or their representative) to request a review whenever they want one.'*

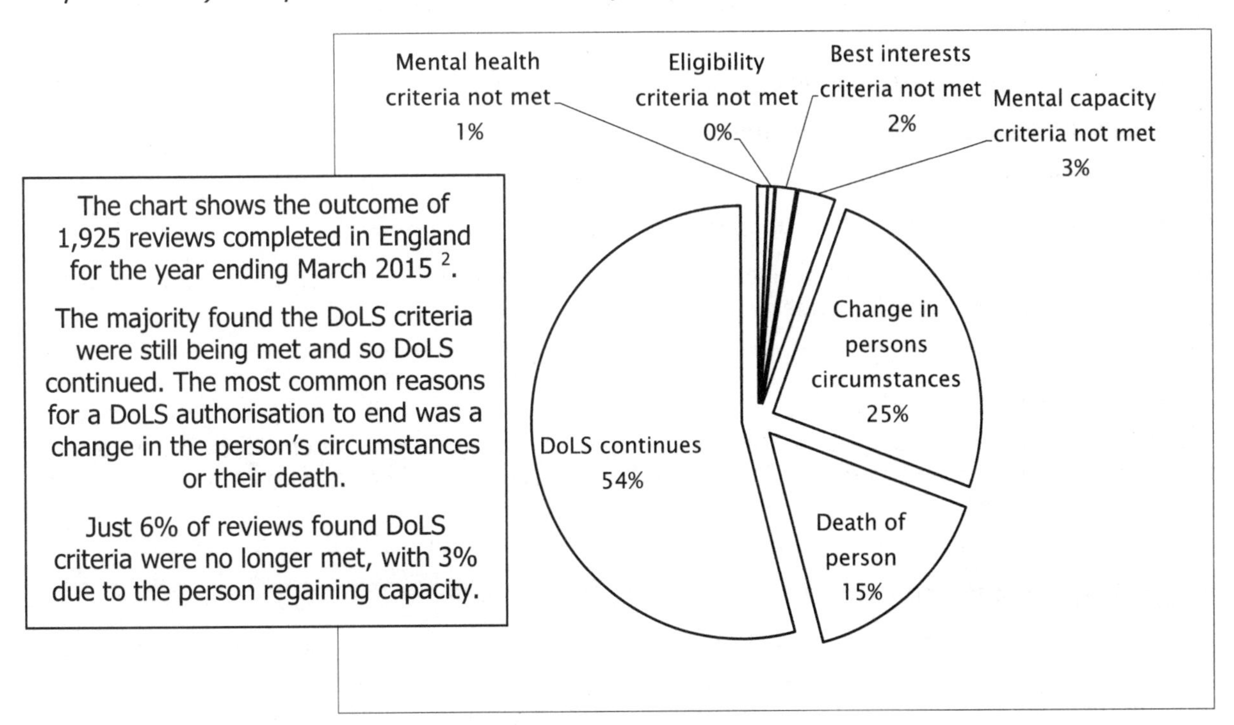


The chart shows the outcome of 1,925 reviews completed in England for the year ending March 2015 [2].

The majority found the DoLS criteria were still being met and so DoLS continued. The most common reasons for a DoLS authorisation to end was a change in the person's circumstances or their death.

Just 6% of reviews found DoLS criteria were no longer met, with 3% due to the person regaining capacity.

## The Court of Protection

Any person under a DoLS authorisation and their representative has a direct right of appeal to the Court of Protection. In addition, any other person can apply to the court about a DoLS but would need permission to do so. The Court of Protection deals solely with cases involving the Mental Capacity Act including DoLS.

---

### Contact details

Court of Protection, PO Box 70185, First Avenue House, 42-49 High Holborn, London WC1A 9JA

Enquiries: 0300 456 4600 Monday to Friday, 10am to 4pm

Email: courtofprotectionenquiries@hmcts.gsi.gov.uk

Website: *www.gov.uk/courts-tribunals/court-of-protection*

The court can also be contacted out of office hours for emergency applications on: 020 7947 6000

---

### Facts and figures

The increase in the number of DoLS cases following the Supreme Court ruling has led to an increase in the number of DoLS cases going to the Court of Protection. Applications to the court relating to deprivation of liberty increased almost fivefold from 109 in 2013 to 525 in 2014 and the latest figures indicate there were 236 applications in the first quarter of 2015 alone[19]. Of these applications almost half related to 'community' deprivation of liberty orders for people not in a care home or hospital and therefore not covered by DoLS.

---

### Applications to the court

Applications to the court can be made where there is a dispute about:

- whether the person meets the standard DoLS criteria, for example whether the person has capacity
- whether an urgent authorisation should have been given
- the duration of a standard or urgent authorisation
- the purpose for which an urgent or standard authorisation is given
- the conditions attached to a standard authorisation

**Note:** A court application should be made for a person that is objecting (verbally or otherwise) to being in a care home or hospital under DoLS.

---

### Powers of the court

The court can vary the duration or terminate an urgent or standard DoLS. Alternatively it may direct the local authority involved to do so (for standard authorisations) or the care home or hospital (for urgent authorisations).

---

### Who can apply to the court?

Applications can be made by the person under DoLS (or any person who lacks or is alleged to lack capacity), their representative, an attorney, a deputy, anyone already named in an existing court order (if the application relates to the order) and for a person who is not yet 18 anyone with parental responsibility for them. All these people can apply to the court without permission (directly). Others, such as local authorities and advocates (IMCAs), can also apply to the court but must seek permission from the court first.

The DoLS Code of Practice (para 10.5) states: '*Wherever possible, concerns about the deprivation of liberty should be resolved informally or through the relevant supervisory body's or managing authority's complaints procedure, rather than through the Court of Protection'.* It continues (para 10.6): *'The aim should be to limit applications to the Court of Protection to cases that genuinely need to be referred to the court. However, with deprivation of liberty at stake, people should not be discouraged from making an application to the Court of Protection if it proves impossible to resolve concerns satisfactorily through other routes in a timely manner.'*

The court has stated a number of times (most recently in the case of *P v Surrey CC & Surrey Downs CCG [2015] EWCOP 54)* that local authorities are expected to be proactive and cannot simply inform families they can appeal if they are not happy. If a local authority knows that family or friends of a person do not believe they should be subject to DoLS or are not in an appropriate placement the local authority should take the lead and apply to the Court of Protection.

For further information on the Court of Protection rules, application process and fees visit: *www.gov.uk/courts-tribunals/court-of-protection*

---

**Damages**

The court can award damages and costs where it finds a person has been unlawfully deprived of their liberty or for other breaches of the Human Rights Act. The awards can vary from a nominal figure to substantial amounts of money. In a recent case *(Essex County Council v RF & Others [2015] EWCOP 1)* involving an elderly man who was removed from his home to a care home following safeguarding concerns, the court ordered damages and costs totalling between £130,000-£150,000. The court found the man had been unlawfully deprived of his liberty in the care home and also his right to private and family life (Article 8 ECHR) had been unlawfully breached.

---

**Deprivation of liberty not in a care home or hospital**

If it is considered necessary to deprive a person of their liberty in a location that is not a care home or hospital this can only be authorised by an order from the Court of Protection (see page 121 for further details). This is outside the DoLS procedures described above and authority would come from the court order that was issued. The court has produced guidance and specific forms for such cases. These can be downloaded from their website.

## Leave of Absence, Absconding, Conveyance and Transfers

The Court of Protection in the cases of *P (Scope of Schedule A1) [2010] COP 30/6/10* and *DCC v KH [2009] COP 11729380* have confirmed that as DoLS authorises deprivation of liberty it implicitly provides the authority to prevent a person leaving a place and this can include using force if necessary and proportionate to do so. This also includes the power to return them if they refuse to return. Although the judge in the earlier case explicitly agreed that the standard authorisation being in place was sufficient to return the person even if the journey amounted to a deprivation of liberty, it would be appropriate to take legal advice. An application to the Court of Protection may need to be considered as this area has not yet been extensively tested in the Court of Protection. In a recent Upper Tribunal case comparing guardianship and DoLS, *NM v Kent County Council [2015] UKUT 125 (AAC)*, the Judge gave the opposing view that it was a *'limitation inherent in DoLS'* that it did not deal with the issue of absconding.

In any event, restraint is allowed to convey or return the person under Sections 5 & 6 Mental Capacity Act. Any actions of restraint require staff in the care home or hospital or others (such as the police) to do a capacity assessment, then (if the person lacks capacity) a best interests assessment and checks on whether the restraint is proportionate and to prevent harm to the person. The power of restraint can be used with or without DoLS being in place as long as it remains a restriction and not a deprivation of liberty.

---

### Leave of absence

Although a person under DoLS is deprived of their liberty, this does not mean they cannot be given leave to go outside the care home or hospital. Such leave may be given with (or without) restrictions such as being escorted or limited in time. Neither the Act nor the Code of Practice provides guidance on how this should be arranged. Unless they are subject to any conditions under the DoLS authorisation it is for care providers to decide on the level of leave a person under DoLS should have. It is recommended that any leave is recorded and reviewed regularly because very limited leave could be questioned in terms of being too restrictive and conversely extended leave (especially unescorted) may call into question whether a person is, or should be, deprived of their liberty at all.

In order to give leave there would be a requirement to assess the person's mental capacity to decide about leave and if they lack capacity a best interests decision should be made. There would be an additional requirement to consider whether any restrictions are to prevent harm to them and proportionate. These assessments may be recorded in the care plan so they can be followed by all staff and reviewed when necessary. Conditions which may be attached to the DoLS authorisation could also apply and the care home or hospital should check for this on the authorisation papers. Care homes and hospitals should have an appropriate leave policy for people under DoLS identifying which staff can authorise leave, how it is recorded and monitored.

It is not lawful to use leave of absence to restrict contact with family or other people the individual is close to. Such actions are an interference of Article 8 ECHR (private and family life) and require authority from the Court of Protection.

---

### Absconding

The Act does not provide details on actions in relation to a resident who absconds from a care home or hospital whilst under DoLS. However, the Court of Protection in the case of *P (Scope of Schedule A1) [2010] COP 30/6/10* confirmed that a person under DoLS can be returned to the care home or hospital using force if necessary and proportionate to the seriousness and likelihood of risk. If a person under DoLS does go absent the police may be contacted. The police would expect to see evidence of the DoLS in place before they are prepared to act as this provides the evidence a person lacks capacity and it is in their best interests to be living in a particular care home or hospital. Local police forces have policies and procedures to address this issue.

Note: If the person who goes absent returns to their own home, for example, and refuses access to the police DoLS does not include a power of entry to barred premises. We would suggest the following options are available for the police to gain entry in such circumstances:

1. An emergency application to the Court of Protection for the power to enter premises. In the case of *Re DD (No.4) (Sterilisation) [2015] EWCOP 4* the judge noted: *'As I have commented in my earlier judgments, section 16(5) of the 2005 Act gives me authority to "make such further orders or give such directions ... as [I] think[s] necessary or expedient for giving effect to, or otherwise in connection with, an order...". This statutory provision endows the court with a wide jurisdiction, limited essentially by what is lawful, necessary and proportionate, to support its essential orders.'*

They continued: *'As I have previously concluded (see for instance [2014] EWCOP 44 [16]), this section can be used to authorise (albeit at the most extreme end of this ancillary jurisdiction) entry by force into a vulnerable person's home, and...the ability to restrain the person as is necessary and proportionate'.*

2. Section 135 of the Mental Health Act 1983 – a warrant from a justice of the peace authorising entry to premises to assess and/or remove a person to a place of safety. The care home or hospital where the person went absent from can be classed as the place of safety.

3. Section 17(1)(e) of the Police and Criminal Evidence Act 1984 (PACE) – the power to enter and search premises without a warrant to '*save life or limb*' or to prevent *'serious damage to property'.*

---

**Conveyance**

DoLS does not provide explicit authority to convey a person to a care home or hospital when a DoLS is first put into place, however the wider powers of the Act permit this. The MCA Code of Practice (para 6.11) states: *'In some cases, there may be no alternative but to move the person ... In cases where a person lacks capacity to consent, Section 5 of the Act allows carers to carry out actions relating to the move...This applies even if the person continues to object to the move.'*

- ***Question:*** *Can taking a person who resists (conveyance) to a care home or hospital result in a deprivation of liberty?*

It is unlikely that transporting someone to a care home or hospital, particularly in an emergency, would result in a deprivation of liberty. If the person lacked capacity, it would meet the criteria for restraint under the Act. However, the DoLS Code of Practice (para 2.15) states: *'In a very few cases, there may be exceptional circumstances where taking a person to a hospital or a care home amounts to a deprivation of liberty, for example where it is necessary to do more than persuade or restrain the person for the purpose of transportation, or where the journey is exceptionally long'.*

If the journey itself was exceptionally long or the restraint used was very intense, an application to the Court of Protection would be required to authorise the deprivation of liberty in the journey itself. Please also note, objecting mental health patients going to hospital for treatment of their mental disorder would need to be admitted under the powers of the Mental Health Act 1983 instead.

---

**Transfers**

Any DoLS authorisation is specific to the person and the care home or hospital in which they are resident. An authorisation cannot be transferred to another managing authority. If a person is, for example, under DoLS in a care home and is then admitted to hospital, the DoLS does not follow them and the hospital would need to apply for a new DoLS authorisation (if they are deprived of their liberty on the hospital ward). If a person is being assessed for an authorisation in a care home or hospital, they might be moved before the assessment is complete. This would end the assessment taking place.

If a person who is already subject to DoLS is moving to a new care home or hospital it is the responsibility of the new care home or hospital to request a standard authorisation from the local authority (Paragraph 25 Schedule A1). Moving a person between wards of the same hospital site is permissible and does not require a new DoLS authorisation. Within the wording of the Act it may also be possible to move a person between different hospital sites of the same NHS Trust without requiring a new DoLS authorisation although further legal advice should be sought. If a person does change wards a review (see relevant chapter) should be considered depending on the circumstances of the new ward.

An authorisation can be transferred between different supervisory bodies (local authorities) see Part of Schedule A1.

## Ending or Suspending a Standard DoLS Authorisation

The DoLS Code of Practice (para 8.8) states: '*An authorisation only permits deprivation of liberty: it does not mean that a person must be deprived of their liberty where circumstances no longer necessitate it.*' A standard DoLS authorisation can be ended in the following ways:

- **Managing authority** – a care home or hospital should end the deprivation of liberty once it is no longer needed. They must then request a review from the local authority (see page 82).
- **Review** – a review can end a DoLS authorisation (see page 82).
- **Court of Protection** – an application to the court can end an authorisation depending on the decision of the court (see page 84).
- **Expiry of the authorisation** – the fixed time period of the authorisation ends. However, it is suggested that this may not be seen as good practice if a new authorisation is not required to detain the person further. This is because a deprivation of liberty should end as soon as possible and not remain in place because it is due to end soon.
- **The person moves** – if a person moves the DoLS will end as it cannot be transferred to a different care home or hospital (see page 86).
- **The person dies** – if a person dies the DoLS will end (see page 89).
- **Suspended more than 28 days ago** – although a DoLS can be suspended, if this continues beyond 28 days the DoLS will end (see page 88).

Local authorities have a specific form to record and notify others that a standard authorisation has ended (Form 9). The local authority is obliged to inform the person concerned, their representative, the care home or hospital; and every interested person originally consulted during the best interests assessment for the authorisation whenever a standard authorisation ends. In addition the care home or hospital have a duty to inform the CQC.

---

### Suspending DoLS

It is possible to suspend a standard DoLS authorisation for up to 28 days if changes in the person's circumstances mean they no longer meet the *eligibility* requirement of DoLS. A care home or hospital can suspend a standard DoLS for up to 28 days using DoLS Form 7 and send this to the local authority with responsibility for the DoLS. A DoLS authorisation is suspended when:

1. The person is now detained in a hospital under Section 2, 3, 4, 35, 36, 37, 38, 44, 45A, 47, 48 or 51 of the Mental Health Act 1983.
2. The authorisation now conflicts with a requirement imposed upon the person under a community treatment order, guardianship order, conditional discharge or section 17 leave of absence (Mental Health Act 1983).

The local authority (Paragraph 93 Schedule A1) must inform the person concerned, their representative and the care home or hospital that the standard authorisation has been suspended. If within the 28 day period the care home or hospital are satisfied that the person meets the eligibility criteria again (for example, the person is discharged from Section 2 of the Mental Health Act) they must inform the local authority. Once the care home or hospital does this the standard DoLS comes back into force (no longer suspended). The local authority (Paragraph 95 Schedule A1) as soon as practicable must inform the following people that the standard authorisation is no longer suspended, the person concerned, their representative, any IMCA (39A type) and the care home or hospital. Alternatively if a standard authorisation is suspended for more than 28 days then it ceases at the end of the 28 day period beginning from when the care home or hospital notified the local authority of the start of the suspension.

## Further Authorisations

A standard DoLS authorisation cannot be extended for further periods of time. Instead, a fresh application needs to be made and a new DoLS authorisation can be put in place following on from the expiry of the last one. It is the responsibility of the care home or hospital (Paragraph 29 Schedule A1) in which a person is resident to request a further standard DoLS authorisation before it expires using DoLS Form 2 (request for a further standard authorisation). Different local authorities may have different policies on the notice period they require, for example two or four weeks. The DoLS Code of Practice (para 3.19) states:

*'There is no statutory limit on how far in advance of the expiry of one authorisation a fresh authorisation can be sought. Clearly, however, an authorisation should not be applied for too far in advance as this may prevent an assessor from making an accurate assessment of what the person's circumstances will be at the time the authorisation will come into force'.*

The new DoLS application means the assessment process takes place again and the local authority must approve the new authorisation if appropriate and state its duration. If a care home or hospital requests a further standard DoLS authorisation it must (Paragraph 84 Schedule A1) inform the person concerned.

---

**Urgent authorisations**

Unlike standard authorisations, urgent authorisations cannot be extended or renewed beyond the maximum 14 days. In addition once an urgent authorisation has been completed it cannot be followed by another at any point in the detention period. (See the case of *A County Council v MB [2010] EWHC 2508 (COP).*)

## Death of a person when under DoLS

The death of a person when under DoLS must be reported to the local coroner. In December 2014 the Chief Coroner of England and Wales issued official guidance[25] as follows: *'... on the law as it now stands, the death of a person subject to a DoL should be the subject of a coroner investigation because that person was in state detention within the meaning of the Coroners and Justice Act 2009.'*

The full guidance can be downloaded from:

*www.judiciary.gov.uk/publications/guidance-no-16-deprivation-of-liberty-safeguards-dols*

The Chief Coroner's guidance[25] also stated:

*'In many cases of this kind which are uncontroversial the inquest may be a 'paper' inquest, decided in open court but on the papers without witnesses having to attend. Intelligent analysis of relevant information (without the need for a post-mortem examination) may be the best approach. Bereaved families should have all of this explained to them in advance.'*

It should be noted that each local coroner has discretion to apply the guidance as they see fit. There is a standard DoLS Form 12 (see page 126) designed for care homes and hospitals to report the deaths of those under DoLS and meet their obligations in this matter.

## Unauthorised Deprivation of Liberty and Failed Assessments

The DoLS Code of Practice (para 9.0) states: *'It is a serious issue to deprive someone of their liberty without authorisation if they lack the capacity to consent. If anyone believes that a person is being deprived of their liberty without authorisation, they should raise this with the relevant authorities.'*

Where there is a concern that a person is being deprived of their liberty but no application has been made to authorise this by the care home or hospital, the Act (Paragraph 68 Schedule A1) provides the means for family or any person to take action. The person themselves, any relative, friend, carer or other third party (such as an advocate) should first approach the care home or hospital who may be able to lessen the restrictions placed on the person so they are no longer deprived of their liberty. Unless the person is to be discharged, it would be very difficult to avoid the deprivation of liberty and so the care home or hospital should apply for an authorisation. The DoLS Code of Practice (para 9.1) states: *'Given the seriousness of deprivation of liberty, a managing authority must respond within a reasonable time to the request. This would normally mean within 24 hours.'*

If the care home or hospital fails to take action in a reasonable period of time, the person who raised the issue may go directly to the local authority and tell them of their concerns. The local authority can decide not to take any action if the request is frivolous or vexatious. The DoLS Code of Practice (para 9.5) describes this as when: *'... the person is very obviously not deprived of their liberty) or where a very recent assessment has been carried out and repeated requests are received ...'* If the issue of an unauthorised deprivation of liberty has already been investigated by the local authority and there has been no change of circumstances since then, they are also not required to take action.

If the local authority decides to carry out an assessment in response to such a request, it must complete it within seven days. The purpose of this assessment is to check whether a deprivation of liberty is in fact taking place. It must be undertaken by a best interests assessor. The assessor must speak to and consult the care home or hospital, the person who raised the concern, the person allegedly being deprived of their liberty and any family or friends (as is practicable to do so). If there are no family or friends who are appropriate to consult, the local authority must appoint an advocate.

The local authority must notify the person who raised the concern, the relevant person, the care home or hospital and any IMCA (39A type) involved of the request and the decision reached. If the person who raised the concern is not satisfied, they can apply to challenge this in the Court of Protection.

---

**Failed assessments (negative conclusion) authorisation not granted**

If the criteria for any of the six assessments (the qualifying requirements) are not met an authorisation cannot be granted (Form 6). This is known as a failed assessment. Any incomplete assessments must stop as soon as this is established. If this happens, the care home or hospital must end an urgent authorisation if one is already in place and, where there is no urgent authorisation in place, reduce or remove the restrictions the person is under to ensure they are not being deprived of their liberty. The DoLS Code of Practice (para 5.24) states: *'The steps taken to stop the deprivation of liberty should be recorded in the care plan. Where possible family, friends and carers should be involved in deciding how to prevent the unauthorised deprivation of liberty from continuing. If the supervisory body has any doubts about whether the matter is being satisfactorily resolved within an appropriately urgent timescale, it should alert the inspection body.'*

The local authority is required (Paragraph 58 Schedule A1) to inform the care home or hospital, the person who was being assessed, any advocate involved and every interested person who was consulted by the best interests assessor whenever it decides not to grant an authorisation. This must be done as soon as practicable after the local authority is aware that an authorisation will not be granted. In addition (Paragraph 135 Schedule A1) all those named earlier must be sent copies of the assessments that were carried out despite the authorisation not being granted. The local authority must keep a written record of all assessments that fail. If a person is deprived of their liberty but DoLS cannot be applied then other legal powers should be used to authorise the deprivation of liberty such as the Mental Health Act 1983 or the Court of Protection, where appropriate.

## The Assessors

A minimum of two assessors, a mental health assessor and a best interests assessor (BIA), are required to carry out the six assessments for a standard DoLS authorisation. All assessors must have prior approval from the relevant local authority to carry out their role. Local authorities are responsible for selecting which assessors will undertake a standard authorisation. A number of rules apply to assessors which are designed to prevent any conflicts of interest.

1. The mental health and best interests assessors must be different.
2. An assessor cannot be related to the person being assessed or to someone with a financial interest in the person's care (full definition on page 125).
3. Assessors cannot have a financial interest in the person's care (see page 125).

Although assessors are employed by (or paid by) the local authority, their independence when undertaking assessments is important and the DoLS Code of Practice (para 4.16) states: '*Assessors act as individual professionals and are personally accountable for their decisions. Managing authorities and supervisory bodies must not dictate or seek to influence their decisions.*'

A statutory regulation, *The Mental Capacity (Deprivation of Liberty: Standard Authorisations, Assessments and Ordinary Residence) Regulations 2008 [No. 1858]* governs the appointment of DoLS assessors by local authorities in England. In Wales, the statutory instrument is *The Mental Capacity (Deprivation of Liberty: Assessments, Standard Authorisations and Disputes about Residence) (Wales) Regulations 2009.* The information below refers to the rules for assessors in England, there is some variation for Welsh assessors.

---

### Mental health assessor

A mental health assessor is a doctor who either is approved under Section 12 of the Mental Health Act 1983 or has three years experience of diagnosing and treating mental disorder. In addition, they must have completed the Deprivation of Liberty Safeguards Mental Health Assessors training programme made available by the Royal College of Psychiatrists. Thereafter, the local authority must be satisfied that the person has, in the 12 months prior to selection, completed further training relevant to their role as a mental health assessor. In choosing the mental health assessor, the Code of Practice states that the aim should be, if possible, to use an assessor who already knows the person. The mental health assessor can undertake three of the six DoLS assessments:

1. Mental health assessment
2. Mental capacity assessment
3. Eligibility assessment

As a minimum they are required to undertake the mental health assessment. Depending on the circumstances of the case, or the practice of the local authority involved, they may also undertake one or both of the other assessments above.

Training to qualify as a mental health assessor is available in a number of ways. The Royal College of Psychiatrists offers an online course and *Edge training and consultancy* (of which both authors of this handbook are directors, see *www.edgetraining.org.uk*) deliver (a legally updated) programme made available by The Royal College of Psychiatrists for both qualification as a mental health assessor and annual update training. Edge also provide annual update/refresher training.

---

### Best interests assessor (BIA)

A best interests assessor is a social worker, nurse, occupational therapist or chartered psychologist with at least two years post registration experience or an approved mental health professional (AMHP). In addition, they must have completed an approved BIA qualification course and then undertake further training related to the role of a BIA every 12 months thereafter (Edge training and consultancy of which both authors of this handbook are directors, see *www.edgetraining.org.uk* deliver BIA legal update courses). In England training to qualify as a BIA is undertaken through approved university courses. Wales has different rules about qualification courses. If a BIA fails to undertake further training during a 12 month period they are not be able to continue as a BIA. However they do not have to retake the BIA qualification course again to practice, rather they would just need to attend a training day related to their role (normally called a BIA legal update). In practice, if a number of years of refresher training have been missed, it would be wise for an assessor to undertake more than one training day. In addition further reading on the case law they have missed in the intervening years will be necessary. Regulations also state that the local authority must be satisfied the BIA has the skills necessary to obtain, evaluate and analyse complex evidence and differing views and to weigh them appropriately in decision making. Finally, the person must not be suspended from the professional register of their own professional body.

In contrast to the mental health assessor, the best interests assessor cannot be involved in the care of the person they assess or in making decisions about the person's care. They cannot be in a line management relationship with the mental health assessor or the person proposing the authorisation. They can, however, be an employee of the local authority or care home or hospital. The exception to this rule is where the supervisory body and the managing authority are the same (for example a care home run by a local authority). In this situation, the best interests assessor cannot be an employee of either organisation or providing services to it.

The Code of Practice comments: '*It is essential that the best interests assessor provides an independent and objective view of whether or not there is a genuine justification for deprivation of liberty, taking account of all the relevant views and factors.*'

Best interests assessors can complete the following DoLS assessments:

1. Age  2. Mental capacity  3. No refusals  4. Best interests  5. Eligibility

(Note: A BIA can only carry out an eligibility assessment if they are also qualified as an AMHP.)

In Wales the health and social care inspectorate bodies have found[8]: '*The Best Interest Assessors (BIAs) are a skilled and valuable resource, and across Wales there are a range of experienced professionals undertaking this role. They have a significant impact on influencing the practice of their colleagues as they act as an internal resource/champion within their teams and service areas.*'

---

**Access to records**

Paragraph 131 Schedule A1 provides DoLS assessors with the legal authority to access, examine and photocopy any health, local authority or care home record they consider relevant to their assessment.

---

**Requirements of assessors**

The statutory regulations state that for a person to be eligible to undertake a DoLS assessment the local authority must be satisfied that:

1. they are insured in respect of any liabilities that might arise in connection with carrying out the assessment.
2. the person has the skills and experience appropriate to the assessment to be carried out which must include, but are not limited to, the following — (a) an applied knowledge of the Mental Capacity Act 2005 and related Code of Practice and (b) the ability to keep appropriate records and to provide clear and reasoned reports in accordance with legal requirements and good practice.
3. they have a satisfactory Disclosure and Barring Service check.

---

**Duty in relation to representatives and IMCAs**

DoLS assessors are required (Paragraph 132 Schedule A1) to '...take into account any information given, or submissions made...' by a representative or an appointed IMCA.

## **The Supervisory Body** (local authority or health board)

The DoLS procedure works on the basis of two bodies or organisations working together. These are known in the Act as the *supervisory body* and the *managing authority.* These titles are only found in DoLS. The supervisory body is the local authority in England or the health board in Wales where a person is ordinarily resident. For ease of use this handbook uses the term local authority when discussing the role of the supervisory body.

Each local authority will normally have a DoLS or MCA manager or coordinator and other staff to help organise the DoLS procedures. If a care provider or others have questions about DoLS they should contact their local authority DoLS team (they may be within the adult safeguarding team). Health and social care inspectors[8] have described them as '*...the linchpin of the system and it was often their personal commitment that had the biggest impact on the quality and quantity of applications.*'

---

### Ordinary residence

In the majority of cases it is not difficult to identify ordinary residence however some situations do present particular problems and there is extensive case law on this issue. Guidance on ordinary residence is available from: *www.gov.uk/government/collections/ordinary-residence-pages*

---

### Local authority duties and responsibilities

Local authorities have a number of duties and responsibilities under DoLS which are detailed below. The main responsibility is to organise assessments for standard authorisations and if the criteria are met to grant a standard authorisation. The DoLS Code of Practice (page 106) states: '*The complete process of assessing and authorising deprivation of liberty should be clearly recorded, and regularly monitored and audited, as part of an organisation's governance structure.*' A theme of DoLS case law has been the court's interpretation of the ongoing and extensive responsibilities of local authorities within the DoLS legislation itself and also the wider expectations of the European Convention on Human Rights towards people deprived of their liberty.

The Association of Directors of Adult Social Services (ADASS) has issued guidance: *Mental Capacity Act including the Deprivation of Liberty Safeguards, an improvement tool* which is available from *www.adass.org.uk*

---

### Granting authorisations and the role of authorising signatories

The DoLS legislation states that local authorities: '*... must give a standard authorisation if – (a) all the assessments are positive ...*' (Paragraph 50 Schedule A1). Giving a standard authorisation means the DoLS is agreed and comes into effect. The process of granting an authorisation means a senior manager from the local authority (generally known as a DoLS authorising signatory) will have checked all the assessments meet the statutory criteria of DoLS and will then grant the authorisation on behalf of the local authority (DoLS Form 5). See page 127 for guidance on what authorising signatories should look for in the completed DoLS assessment forms when granting a standard authorisation.

The importance and significance of the role of the authorising signatory was highlighted in the case of *London Borough of Hillingdon v Neary & Anor [2011] EWCOP 1377.* In this case the judge was highly critical of the local authority for granting four standard authorisations based on poorly evidenced best interests assessments. The judge stated:

*'The responsibilities of a supervisory body, correctly understood, require it to scrutinise the assessment it receives with independence and a degree of care that is appropriate to the seriousness of the decision and to the circumstances of the individual case that are or should be known to it. Where, as here, a supervisory body grants authorisations on the basis of perfunctory scrutiny of superficial best interests assessments, it cannot expect the authorisations to be legally valid.'*

The judge found the local authority had failed to properly scrutinise the assessments it received and given their poor quality, the judge found all the authorisations granted to be so flawed that they did not constitute a lawful basis for deprivation of liberty.

Recent case law *(P v Surrey CC & Surrey Downs CCG [2015] EWCOP 54)* has reiterated that the role of an authorising signatory is active rather than passive. In this case, concerning a DoLS standard authorisation, there was a question over whether the current placement for the individual concerned was appropriate and if other less restrictive placements were available instead. The judge stated: *'The first respondent* [local authority] *had the duty to investigate whether a less restrictive alternative was available ... It already knew that the care home was not suitable in the medium or longer term because it had been told so by the social worker undertaking the best interests assessment. Being in possession of that knowledge, the obligation was on the first respondent* [local authority] *to be proactive, and they failed in that obligation.'*

The CQC, in its annual DoLS report[10], noted: *'... given the complexity of the Safeguards system and the ongoing developments in case law we would expect all local authorities to make sure their signatories have access to appropriate training so they can fulfil their role with up-to-date knowledge.'* Edge training and consultancy of which both authors are directors delivers a course for DoLS authorising signatories (www.edgetraining.org.uk).

---

**Assessors**

The local authority is responsible for selecting which assessors will carry out a standard authorisation assessment (Paragraph 129 Schedule A1). In addition they are responsible for ensuring the assessors they use meet the requirements given in the legislation and statutory regulations. Each local authority will have a list of assessors it considers are qualified to carry out assessments within its area.

---

**Urgent authorisations**

When an urgent authorisation ceases, the local authority is obliged (Paragraph 90 Schedule A1), as soon as practicable, to inform the person concerned and any IMCA (39A type).

---

**Copies of assessments**

Paragraph 135 Schedule A1 places a duty on local authorities to give copies of all completed standard authorisation assessments to the care home or hospital, the person being assessed, their representative and any appointed IMCA (Section 39A type). This should be done when the local authority is notifying these parties that a standard authorisation has been granted (see below). The same duty to provide a copy of assessments (except to representatives) applies even when a standard authorisation is not granted (Paragraph 135(4)) and when a standard DoLS is reviewed (Paragraph 135(5)) including any 39D IMCA.

---

**Providing information**

Local authorities have a duty (Paragraph 57 Schedule A1) to give a copy of all completed standard authorisations as soon as practicable to:

1. the representative
2. the care home or hospital (managing authority)
3. the person under DoLS
4. every interested person who was consulted by the BIA for the DoLS assessment
5. any Section 39A IMCA

The same duty applies (except there will be no representative) even when the local authority does not grant an authorisation following the assessment process (Paragraph 58 Schedule A1).

*Authorisation ceases:* when a standard authorisation ceases to be in force the local authority must, as soon as practicable, notify everyone listed above 1 to 4 but not the IMCA (39A).

*Urgent authorisation extension requests:* when a care home or hospital requests an extension of an urgent DoLS, the local authority is obliged (Paragraph 86 Schedule A1) to notify the care home or hospital of its decision and the duration of the extension if applicable. If the decision is not to extend the urgent DoLS the local authority must give reasons for this.

*Suspension of standard authorisations:* the local authority (Paragraph 93 Schedule A1) must inform the person concerned, their representative and the care home or hospital.

*Reviews:* when a review of a standard authorisation is to be undertaken, the local authority must inform the person under DoLS, their representative and the care home or hospital (Paragraph 108 Schedule A1). In addition, when the outcome is known the same people must be informed. If an IMCA is involved (39D type) the local authority only has to inform them of the outcome of a review. Local authorities must keep a record of all requests for reviews (Paragraph 120 Schedule A1) and their outcomes (Paragraph 121 Schedule A1).

*Appointment of representatives:* whenever a representative is appointed the local authority must send a copy of the written appointment to everyone listed above 1-5 plus any person acting as a lasting power of attorney or deputy for the person concerned (DoLS Code of Practice, para 7.23).

---

**Representatives**

Although BIAs can recommend a person to become the representative as part of their assessment, it is the local authority that is responsible for appointing them (Paragraph 139 Schedule A1). Mr Justice Baker in the Court of Protection *(AJ v A Local Authority [2015] EWCOP 5)* stated the following: *'... the local authority ought not to have appointed Mr. C as RPR notwithstanding the fact that he was selected by the BIA. The European and domestic case law make it clear that there is a positive duty on public authorities under the Convention to ensure that a person deprived of liberty is not only entitled but enabled to have the lawfulness of his detention reviewed speedily by a court ...'*

The ongoing duty of local authorities to monitor the actions of representatives once appointed was also highlighted by Mr Justice Baker (case of AJ cited above): *'Having (in my judgment wrongly) appointed Mr. C as RPR, the local authority as the supervisory body ought to have quickly realised (1) that AJ was extremely unhappy in residential care and wished to challenge the authorisations and (2) that Mr. C was not taking any or any sufficient steps to represent or support her in pursuing that challenge. The local authority should therefore have taken steps to replace Mr C as RPR when it became apparent that he was not intending to issue proceedings promptly and that there was not going to be a speedy review of AJ's detention by a court ...'*

---

**Record of requests and authorisations**

Paragraph 60 Schedule A1 places a legal duty on local authorities to keep a written record of all standard authorisations they have granted and also requests for standard authorisations which they have not granted. In addition Paragraph 84 Schedule A1 places a duty to keep a written record of all requests for extensions of urgent DoLS, the outcome and the period of the extension authorised. If the local authority decides not to agree an extension this must also be recorded.

---

**Reviews**

Local authorities must respond to requests for reviews and decide which criteria needs to be reviewed. The local authority then has responsibility for assigning assessors to carry out a review and based on the outcome continue the standard authorisation or end it (see page 82).

---

**Independent mental capacity advocates (IMCA)**

Local authorities are responsible for making referrals for IMCAs within the DoLS procedures. Further information on the role and referral criteria for IMCAs is given on page 79.

## The Positive Duty on Local Authorities

Under DoLS, it is the responsibility of care homes and hospitals to identify residents and patients who lack capacity and may be deprived of their liberty. The legislation then requires them to make an application to the local authority to arrange the necessary assessments. If a care home or hospital fails to refer a person for a DoLS assessment then family members or any other person who believes someone is deprived of their liberty can contact the local authority (see page 90).

It could therefore appear that the local authority's role is passive as they wait for referrals to be made to them in their role as the supervisory body. However, this is not the case in practice and local authorities are required to be proactive and identify people they have placed into care homes who could be deprived of their liberty and act on this without having to wait for a referral from the care home or hospital. The reasons for this are:

---

1. **The European Convention on Human Rights** places a positive duty on the state to protect people's rights. This means that state bodies (local authorities, NHS Trusts, CCGs, CQC ) and their staff who could, or should, be reasonably aware of a person who is deprived of their liberty must take action to firstly try and bring an end to the deprivation of liberty if possible. If this is not possible they need to ensure it is legally authorised by DoLS or a Court of Protection application (if the person is not in a care home or hospital).

   The Supreme Court in the Cheshire West ruling noted: '... *the first sentence of article 5(1) must be construed as laying down a positive obligation on the state to protect the liberty of those within its jurisdiction ... The state is therefore obliged to take measures providing effective protection of vulnerable persons, including reasonable steps to prevent a deprivation of liberty of which the authorities have or ought to have knowledge.'*

---

2. **Case law** has consistently shown that if a person is unlawfully deprived of their liberty, it is the local authority which placed the person in the care home that is held responsible. Case examples are numerous and include the following:

   *London Borough of Hillingdon v Neary & Anor [2011] EWCOP 1377*
   *A Local Authority v Mr & Mrs D [2013] EWHC B34*
   *Somerset County Council v MK [2014] EWCOP B25*
   *Essex County Council v RF & Others [2015] EWCOP 1*

   In each case above the unlawful deprivation of liberty identified by the court was ultimately deemed to be the responsibility of the local authority that placed the person there.

---

3. **The Local Government Ombudsman** has ruled against a local authority who tried to claim it was a care home's responsibility for failing to identify a deprivation of liberty for a person placed in the care home by the local authority. The Ombudsman[17] stated: *'We note the Council's comment that it was the care home's responsibility. However, under s25(7) of the Local Government Act 1974, any action taken by the home is considered to be taken on behalf of the Council and in the exercise of its functions.'*

---

4. **Before a person is even placed in a care home or hospital**, consideration and referral for a DoLS assessment should be made. In the case of *AJ v A Local Authority [2015] EWCOP 5*, Mr Justice Baker stated: '...*in the vast majority of cases, it should be possible to plan in advance so that a standard authorisation can be obtained before the deprivation of liberty begins. It is only in exceptional cases, where the need for the deprivation of liberty is so urgent that it is in the best interests of the person for it to begin while the application is being considered, that a standard authorisation need not be sought before the deprivation begins.*'

(Note: If a CCG places a person under continuing healthcare they would be responsible and should contact the DoLS team if the care home doesn't act themselves)

## **The Managing Authority** (care home or hospital)

The managing authority under DoLS is the care home or hospital where the person lacking capacity is resident. For hospitals the managing authority will be the NHS Trust or private organisation responsible for managing the hospital where the patient is resident. For care homes it is the registered care home manager (private or local authority) who takes on the role of managing authority. A care home is one that is registered as such under the terms of the Health and Social Care Act 2008. The DoLS Code of Practice (para 3.21) states that if the managing authority and supervisory body are the same organisation: '*This does not prevent it from acting in both capacities. However in England the regulations specify that in such a situation, the best interests assessor cannot be an employee of the supervisory body/managing authority, or providing services to it.*'

---

### Legal duties on care homes and hospitals

DoLS places a number of legal duties on care homes and hospitals in their role as the managing authority under the Act. It is important that care homes and hospitals have systems in place to ensure they can show evidence of compliance with these duties. The CQC can be expected to look at whether these legal obligations under DoLS are being met.

---

### Identifying residents who are deprived of their liberty

It is the responsibility of care homes and hospitals to identify which of their residents may be deprived of their liberty under DoLS (Paragraphs 24-26 Schedule A1). The duty relates to people who are already resident and also those who are likely to be resident in the next 28 days. In either case if the resident of the care home or hospital is, or is likely to be, deprived of their liberty within the next 28 days (and meets all the DoLS criteria) they are required to request a standard authorisation.

To do this care homes and hospitals need to assess whether the individual concerned can consent to admission. Those people who lack capacity to consent should then be screened to see if they may be deprived of their liberty (see pages 100 and 101 for a procedure chart and a screening tool). This would need to be an ongoing process as some residents who have capacity on admission may, over time, lose their capacity regarding this decision.

If, after assessment, the local authority concludes that a person does not meet the DoLS criteria the care home or hospital is not required to request another standard authorisation unless it appears there has been a change in the person's case which means the local authority would now be likely to give a standard authorisation (Paragraph 28 Schedule A1).

---

### Providing information

A care home or hospital requesting a standard authorisation is obliged (Paragraph 31 Schedule A1) to provide certain information to the local authority (DoLS Form 1). In addition the care home or hospital must give the best interests assessor a copy of any relevant needs assessment and care plan (Paragraph 39 Schedule A1) for the person being assessed.

---

### Information on rights

When an urgent or standard authorisation is granted, the care home or hospital has a legal duty (Paragraphs 59 and 83 Schedule A1) to inform the person of their rights both orally and in writing. In addition, they must take all practicable steps to ensure the person understands their rights.

The information must include details about the:

- effect of the authorisation
- right to appeal to the Court of Protection
- right to request a review (not applicable for urgent authorisations)
- right to an advocate and how to get one appointed (not applicable for urgent authorisations)

For standard authorisations, the representative must also be informed in writing of these rights. An example of a rights leaflet is provided at page 136.

Note: If an IMCA (39D) is appointed the care home or hospital must also give them a copy of the written information above.

The CQC[10] has stated: *'It is essential that hospitals, care homes and local authorities fulfil their statutory duty to explain to people who are subject to the Deprivation of Liberty Safeguards, their representatives, their families and close friends their rights and how to challenge the authorisation.'*

---

**Urgent authorisations**

The DoLS Code of Practice (para 6.11) notes that when considering an urgent authorisation the care home or hospital: *'...must, as far as is practicable and possible, take account of the views of anyone engaged in caring for the relevant person or interested in their welfare.'*

When completing an urgent authorisation, care homes and hospitals must, as soon as practicable, give a copy of the authorisation to the person placed under an urgent DoLS authorisation and any Section 39A IMCA appointed (Paragraph 82 Schedule A1). If a care home or hospital requests an extension of an urgent DoLS beyond seven days (Paragraph 84 Schedule A1) they must inform the person concerned they are doing this and then inform the person of the outcome once the local authority has made a decision by giving them a copy of the decision. The care home or hospital is also required, as far as possible and appropriate, to inform the person's family, friends and carers that an urgent authorisation has been made so that they can support the person concerned. Standard authorisations do not place the same duties on care homes and hospitals as the local authority is responsible for them.

---

**Further authorisations**

Care homes and hospitals are responsible (Paragraph 29 Schedule A1) for requesting further authorisation to standard authorisations at least 28 days before they are due to expire and they must inform the person concerned they have done this. This is done using DoLS Form 2.

---

**Access to records for DoLS assessors**

DoLS assessors are legally entitled to examine and take copies of any health, local authority or care home records they consider relevant to their assessment (Paragraph 131 Schedule A1). Care homes and hospitals should therefore ensure their access to records policy reflects this.

---

**Care and treatment**

Care and treatment for people under DoLS is authorised by the Mental Capacity Act if the person lacks capacity about that care or treatment. This requires assessments of capacity and best interests by the care provider following the normal operation of the Act.

---

**The representative**

For residents under a standard DoLS authorisation, care homes and hospitals need to record the details of the person's representative (who may not be an immediate family member) and ensure staff understand the role of this person. In addition care providers are required to monitor how often a representative visits (DoLS Code of Practice, para 7.27) and inform the local authority if they have concerns. Given the statutory role of the representative, care providers should ensure they are invited to attend key care planning meetings and are consulted on significant decisions relating to the care of the person. It should be noted, however, that representatives are not responsible for making decisions about the care or treatment of the person under DoLS. Decisions about care or treatment rest with those delivering care or otherwise with people specifically authorised to make such decisions (personal welfare lasting power of attorney or deputy).

---

## Monitoring

As indicated above, the duty to request a further DoLS authorisation when one is about to expire rests with the care home or hospital (Paragraph 29 Schedule A1). Care homes and hospitals therefore need to have a monitoring system in place that prompts staff to contact the local authority to request a reassessment of DoLS when a standard authorisation is due to expire. The prompt should be some weeks before the expiry to give the local authority time to arrange fresh assessments. This monitoring also needs to look at whether the person continues to meet all the DoLS criteria and if not request a review from the local authority. Health and social care inspectors have found[8]: '*The care homes visited were not always aware of their responsibilities to monitor and request reviews and relied heavily on the Supervisory Bodies to prompt them.*'

---

## Notification of DoLS requests and outcomes

Care homes and hospitals must notify CQC of all applications to deprive someone of their liberty (and their outcomes) whether through DoLS or by applying to the Court of Protection. The CQC has a standard online form for this at www.cqc.org.uk. In addition care homes and hospitals have a statutory duty (Paragraphs 32, 82 and 84 Schedule A1) to keep a written record of all standard DoLS requests, urgent DoLS authorisations and requests for further authorisations of standard DoLS authorisations. In each case the reasons why the requests were made or urgent authorisation given must also be recorded.

---

## DoLS forms

Care homes and hospitals need to ensure they have accessible copies of the necessary DoLS forms (paper or electronic) to make referrals and carry out their other duties. In addition, for patients or residents under DoLS the completed DoLS authorisation must be stored safely and the care records should clearly indicate to staff the legal status of the individual.

---

## Conditions

A DoLS authorisation can have conditions attached to it and the legislation states: '*... the relevant hospital or care home must ensure that any conditions are complied with*' (Paragraph 53 Schedule A1). Staff therefore should ensure any conditions attached to a DoLS authorisation are incorporated into care planning records. Care homes and hospitals should monitor whether stated conditions are being met in practice. If they are not, the care home or hospital should inform the local authority to request a review of the conditions. Local authorities are not able to directly enforce compliance with conditions under the Act, however the failure to meet stated conditions can be challenged in the Court of Protection.

---

## Leave of absence

Care homes and hospitals need to ensure they have an appropriate leave of absence policy for people under DoLS. This should identify which staff can authorise such leave, how it is recorded and monitored and the details of the leave agreed, for example escorted by family members (page 86).

---

## Advocacy

Care providers need to be aware of whether an advocate (IMCA) is appointed. Not everyone on DoLS will have an advocate but staff should be clear about whether or not one has been appointed. Staff should also be able to show they know who the local IMCA provider is and have up to date contact details.

---

## Death notification

When a person dies whilst under DoLS the local coroner and CQC must be informed (see page 89).

# Deprivation of Liberty procedure for care providers

**1. Does the person have capacity to decide to stay in a hospital or care home?**
A person may be content or happy in a care home or hospital (or any placement) but that does not mean they have the mental capacity to consent to being there. To have the mental capacity to make a decision the person must be able to:

Understand relevant information + Retain it + Use or weigh the information + Communicate the decision

*(In terms of the relevant information that needs to be understood see page 47).*

**Yes: they have capacity**
(they must be allowed to decide where to live)

**No: they lack capacity – go to next box**

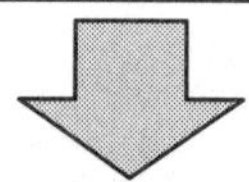

**2. What restrictions are in place?**
A person who lacks capacity to consent to be resident for care will often have restrictions placed on them to ensure they receive the care they need and to keep them safe. Restrictions can take a number of forms: (a) *actual restrictions* such as physical restraint (b) *what if restrictions* – what would staff do if the person stopped washing or tried to leave (c) *restricted access* – access to kitchen (locked), access to outside world (escorted). Consider the type + duration + effect + manner + degree or intensity of each restriction in the care plan (Guzzardi v Italy 1980).

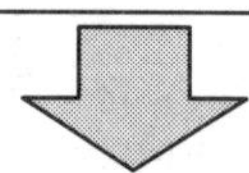

**3. Do the restrictions mean the person is under *complete supervision and control AND not free to leave*?**

**Complete supervision and control?** This usually (often) means 24 hour care provision but it does not have to mean one to one staffing. It could involve a number of actions such as not allowing the person out alone, controlling what they do during the day or when they eat and go to sleep. A person can be under complete supervision and control despite having unescorted leave if the care provider controls when and/or how long a person can go out and when the person must return.

**Not free to leave?** This question is not asking whether the person is free to go out (with or without staff) for an outing of some sort but rather asking whether the person is free to discharge themselves and live somewhere else of their choosing (regardless of whether they actually have the mental capacity to make such a choice).

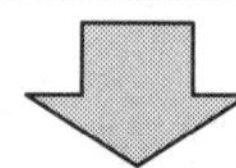

**Yes**
The person is deprived of their liberty, go to the box below.

**No**
The person is not deprived of their liberty. Record the assessment and keep it under review in case the restrictions do become a deprivation of liberty in the future.

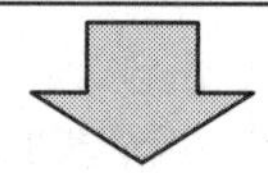

**Are they aged 18 or over and in a registered care home or hospital?**

**Yes** – make a DoLS application using DoLS Form 1 and the local authority will arrange the necessary assessments.

**No** – inform the DoLS team who will provide guidance and support.

**Note:** This chart does not state all the legal criteria required for DoLS or a Court of Protection order.

BOOKSWISE
Download from: www.BooksWise.org.uk

# Deprivation of Liberty Safeguards (DoLS) Screening Tool

DoLS applies to anyone aged 18 or over, who lacks capacity to be resident for care/treatment and is in a registered care home or hospital. **Note:** If a person is living in another place (supported living for example) or is aged 16+ they can be deprived of their liberty under a court order (not under DoLS). In any such situation contact the DoLS office at your local authority.

## 1. List the *restrictions* placed on the person

(Restrictions can include actions or rules that actually enable or support a person to be safe and lead a fulfilling life, for example a person is only allowed out if escorted)

| **Type of restriction**<br>doors locked, escorted outside, physical restraint, medication to manage behaviour, restricted access to kitchen etc | **The restriction in practice**<br>Describe its duration, effect, manner and degree or intensity, for example: how often, for how long, the impact on the individual, the intensity of the restriction – is it regular and ongoing? (For example: Escorted outside for own safety, twice daily, by one member of staff, for x hours. Enables individual to go to college, the shops and clubs.) |
|---|---|
| | |
| | |
| | |
| | |
| | |

## 2. Do the above restrictions mean the person is under *complete supervision and control* AND *not free to leave*?

(If the answer to both elements of this question is **YES** then the person is being deprived of their liberty and you should contact your local DoLS office for advice)

| | |
|---|---|
| **Complete supervision and control?** | This would generally mean 24 hour care provision but it does not have to mean one to one (or in line of sight) staffing. Complete supervision and control could involve a number of actions such as not allowing the person out alone, controlling what they do during the day, determining when they eat and go to sleep. A person can be under complete supervision and control despite having unescorted leave if the care provider controls when the person can go out, for how long and says the person is required to return. |
| **Not free to leave?** | This is not questioning whether the person is free to go out (with or without staff) for an outing but rather whether the person is free to discharge themselves and live somewhere else of their choosing (regardless of whether they actually have the mental capacity to make such a choice.) |

**Note:** A person can legally be classed as deprived of their liberty even if any or all the following are true: 1) The person is compliant with the care received and has never tried to leave. 2) Their family are happy with the placement. 3) The placement is providing excellent care that is appropriate to their needs and in their best interests. 4) The reason the person is in the placement is purely to deliver the care they need and to keep them from coming to harm. 5) The doors are not locked.

## 358 days: A Personal Story of DoLS

What follows is a personal account by Mark Neary of his experience of DoLS in relation to his son, Steven. The resulting court case of *London Borough of Hillingdon v Neary & Anor [2011] EWCOP 1377* is one of the most important to date in relation to DoLS and its application.

---

"2010 was the worst year of my life. For 358 days my son, Steven Neary, was held by the London Borough of Hillingdon in a positive behaviour unit against his and my wishes. During that time, he was held under four deprivation of liberty authorisations. In December 2010, in the High Court, Justice Mostyn terminated the latest authorisation and allowed Steven to return home. In June 2011, in a blaze of publicity, Justice Peter Jackson held that all four DoLS had been unlawful and for a whole year Hillingdon had breached Steven's Article 5 and Article 8 Human Rights. This is my account of wrestling with the Mental Capacity Act in an attempt to get Steven home.

I should say that ultimately, the Deprivation of Liberty Safeguards saved Steven. For all its faults (and there are many), without the DoLS being in place, I have no idea how we would ever have got to court. It is stated many times in the judgment that Hillingdon had an agenda that they chose not to reveal to me or Steven for much of 2010. On the contrary, they led Steven and me to believe that we were in a transition home programme whilst concealing their real agenda, which was to move Steven to a hospital in Wales, under a Section of the Mental Health Act 1983. The judge said: 'if that had happened, Steven would have faced a life in public care that he did not want and does not need'. As a DoLS was in place, we were able to bring the matter to court, expose the extent of Hillingdon's duplicity and give Steven the sort of life that he had been denied for 358 days.

Therefore, because of the hidden agenda, our case was not a typical DoLS case. For starters, Hillingdon completely contrived the authorisations to conceal the real agenda. None of the authorisations made any reference to the fact that being in the unit was the actual deprivation of his liberty. That was one of the biggest battles throughout the year. I had to learn about the Act very quickly and it seemed pretty obvious to me what the deprivation was; but without that recorded it became impossible to challenge. If that was the biggest stumbling block, there were several more that made our access to justice very hard to get. It took seven months to be referred for an IMCA; once we had an IMCA on board, the result was transformative. It is surely a flaw in the system that the person or their representative is completely reliant on the supervisory body who authorised the DoLS to refer you to the IMCA service. To put it bluntly, as in our case, if the authority doesn't want you to have an IMCA, there is no way of getting one. That cannot be right.

In the Neary v Hillingdon judgment, there are repeated references to the safeguarding manager responsible for the DoLS, stating that it was my responsibility to bring the matter before the court. Thankfully, Justice Jackson gave him short shrift on that one. But it's another example of the blocks put in the representative's way if the authority doesn't want their actions scrutinised. Even when I learned that I could bring the matter to court, I foolishly trusted Hillingdon who told me they would be submitting an immediate application to court (they didn't). Now, wiser, I always advise people to apply to the court themselves; it is too risky to leave it up to the supervisory body.

The other big problem I faced when challenging the DoLS process was the best interests assessments. Everything I had read, told me that a BIA must be neutral and, the clue is in the title, was supposed to be acting in the person's best interests. In our case, I spoke to the first two BIAs on the telephone and met the third one face to face but I couldn't get any of them to acknowledge the real deprivation; still less address if the authority's actions were the 'least restrictive option' for Steven's care. This was bewildering to me; how could such fundamental and crucial factors be overlooked? Call me cynical, but it has led me to become very suspicious of the independence of a best interests assessment, if it means the BIA going against their paymaster. In fairness, I was recently invited to speak at a BIA conference and encountered a completely different stance to what I experienced with Hillingdon. But it's an issue; what is the person or their representative to do if their position isn't recorded or they feel that the assessment is fundamentally flawed.

I'm sure it's clear as you read this that I had to learn the Mental Capacity Act very quickly; I received no help at all from Hillingdon because that would have exposed their hidden agenda. I like to see myself as pretty stoic and reasonably intelligent, but my goodness; there were times when I found the legislation impenetrable. A year on, I can be a bit more objective. I was initially thrown by the word 'safeguards'; what was happening to Steven didn't feel like safeguarding. Justice Jackson commented that it was wrong to use the safeguards as an 'instrument of confinement', turning the Mental Capacity Act on its head. Now, when I'm asked for advice from people who have relatives trapped in care homes, I see their nervousness when I suggest they demand their authority initiates the DoLS legislation. A lot of work needs to be done on the image of the legislation; in no small measure because Hillingdon abused it so.

As I said earlier, the DoLS saved Steven's life. Both he and myself as his representative, were automatically entitled to legal aid to challenge the DoLS, just by virtue of a DoLS being in place. That afforded us the excellent representation that we received. Joe Public cannot fight a DoLS on their own; the power imbalance is too great. I would regularly go to review meetings with the council on my own and find there would be eight local authority officials present. It was very intimidating. Independent advocacy and the courts are the best hope for the vulnerable when faced with the might of the supervisory body.

Since our case was published in 2011, a lot of water has flown under the DoLS bridge, some for the good – some not so good. The *Cheshire West* judgment has certainly got supervisory bodies on their toes, which is not a bad thing. I still have my DoLS wish list though: 1) that supervisory bodies are more accountable for their actions; 2) BIAs are allowed to be truly independent; 3) P or their representative to have access to advocacy without relying on a supervisory body referral; 4) supervisory bodies when faced with a case that doesn't fit the criteria for a DoLS to not be allowed to use the MHA and section the person as a trump card; and 5) that the transparency of the Court of Protection continues to blossom. It is crucial for families of a person under DoLS to have information about the person's rights and how to challenge the DoLS. The more cases that are in the public domain, the more helpful that will be for people subject to a DoLS.

To end on a personal note – Steven is happier and more content than he has ever been. In November 2013, Steven was allocated a housing association tenancy, so he now has his own home that I think he is genuinely proud of. For the whole of 2010, he really struggled with communal living and having his own space has allowed him to mature and make choices that are best for him. For me, a whole new career has opened up. I am regularly asked to speak at social care/legal events across the country and the writing career that I put on hold 30 odd years ago has unexpectedly sprung to life again. I think Steven and I are both stronger, wiser people (albeit slightly less trusting than before the illegal detention) and because of that, I feel optimistic about the future."

Mark Neary

*Follow the continuing story of Mark and Steven with regular updates at:*

*www.markneary1dotcom1.wordpress.com*

## DoLS and the Mental Health Act 1983

The reason for DoLS being created was because of a legal case concerning a mental health hospital where the European Court of Human Rights identified a 'gap' in our domestic legislation. The Bournewood case, as it is commonly known, involved a man with a learning disability admitted to a mental health ward. Because he was considered to be compliant with his admission and treatment hospital staff did not use the Mental Health Act 1983 to detain him. Instead he was described as an 'informal' patient. The European Court found his situation on the ward meant he was deprived of his liberty because he was subject to *continuous supervision and control and not free to leave* and he had not consented to it (because he lacked the capacity to consent). However the court found there was no adequate provision in the law of the United Kingdom to authorise this situation. As result of this judgment DoLS created to fill this gap, often known as the 'Bournewood gap'.

---

### Reasons DoLS cannot be used

In the majority of cases the decision about which Act to use is not complex because the criteria of each Act, properly understood and applied, will direct staff to one outcome. For example, if any of the following are true for a person on, or being admitted to, a mental health ward where they could be deprived of their liberty, then DoLS could not be applied.

1. They are under 18 years of age.
2. They present a risk of harm to others and not themselves.
3. They have an advance decision refusing treatment for mental disorder.
4. They have the mental capacity to consent to admission to a mental health ward.
5. They are objecting to admission or treatment for mental disorder.
6. A personal welfare lasting power of attorney or deputy is refusing admission.

All of the above would mean a person does not meet the legal criteria for DoLS and so the only options available would be a voluntary admission (if they consented) or the use of the Mental Health Act 1983 (presuming they meet the criteria for this Act). For DoLS assessors, the check on whether DoLS can be used is called the eligibility assessment (see page 66) which a person must meet for DoLS to be authorised.

---

### When either DoLS or the Mental Health Act could be used

There are situations when either DoLS or the Mental Health Act may be applicable for a person on a mental health ward. The statutory Mental Health Act Code of Practice[20] provides straight forward guidance for mental health staff in relation to this. It states (para 13.49) with emphasis added:

*'If an individual:*

a. *is suffering from a* ***mental disorder*** *(within the meaning of the Act)*

b *needs to be* ***assessed and/or treated in a hospital setting for that disorder*** *or for physical conditions related to that disorder (and meets the criteria for an application for admission under Sections 2 or 3 of the Act)*

c. *has a care treatment package that may or will amount to a* ***deprivation of liberty***

d. ***lacks capacity*** *to consent to being accommodated in the relevant hospital for the purpose of treatment, and*

e. ***does not object*** *to being admitted to hospital, or to some or all the treatment they will receive there for mental disorder.*

*Then in principle a DoLS authorisation (or potentially a Court of Protection order) and detention under the Act would* ***both be available*** *(subject to the assessments required for a DoLS authorisation, including the eligibility assessment). This is the one situation where the option of using either the Act or DoLS exists. It is important to note that a person cannot be detained under the Act at the same time as being subject to a DoLS authorisation or a Court of Protection order.'*

**Why use DoLS in mental health services?**

The following examples explain why mental health services will need to consider the use of DoLS for people using their services. In all of these cases the person has already been assessed and found to lack capacity to be resident for care or treatment.

1. **Discharge from hospital** – a person is discharged from a mental health ward into a care home which is not registered to use the Mental Health Act 1983. The person's care plan may mean they are deprived of their liberty in the care home and this must be authorised. DoLS can be applied for in advance. The care home could therefore make a DoLS application to the local authority.

2. **Physical treatment** – a person needs physical treatment (not related to or arising from their mental disorder) and whilst in the acute general hospital ward they will be subject to complete supervision and control and not free to leave. The Mental Health Act 1983 is limited to the treatment of mental disorder and in this case could not be applied. In addition it should be noted if the person resisted the physical treatment further legal advice should be sought as an application to the Court of Protection may be required.

3. **Learning disability** – to meet the criteria for Section 3 of the Mental Health Act a person's learning disability must be associated with *'abnormally aggressive or seriously irresponsible conduct'* (Section 1(2A)(b) of the Mental Health Act). DoLS does not have this requirement and it could be used instead. This is because if the person remains on the ward and lacks capacity it is likely that the level of care and supervision they would be subject to would amount to a deprivation of their liberty. Note: The criteria of *'abnormally aggressive or seriously irresponsible conduct'* also applies to the application of guardianship, community treatment orders and the majority of forensic sections (Sections 35, 36, 37, 38, 45A, 47, 48 and 51).

4. **The 'compliant incapacitated' patient** – on a mental health ward. In this case either DoLS or the Mental Health Act could be used and practitioners would need to decide which is most appropriate on a case by case basis.

5. **Community Mental Health Act powers** – this relates to people who are discharged into the community under the Mental Health Act subject to community treatment orders, guardianship, conditional discharge or section 17 leave of absence. All four situations could involve care plans that result in a person being deprived of their liberty and this would need to be authorised either by DoLS or a Court of Protection order which can run alongside the Mental Health Act powers.

6. **Article 8 (European Convention on Human Rights) Right to respect for private & family life** – there have been a number of community cases where in order to keep a person safe the associated care plan has involved actions which infringe their Article 8 (Human Rights Act) right to private and family life. A Court of Protection order is required to authorise such action.

---

**Admission to mental health wards**

The Mental Capacity Act has had an enormous impact on how people are admitted to mental health wards. For many people being admitted an assessment of their mental capacity to consent to admission is crucial and must be recorded. The chart on the next page provides a summary of the routes of admission and how the Mental Capacity Act and DoLS fit into this process.

## Admission of Adults to Mental Health Hospitals: Four routes

For a person needing treatment for mental disorder [a]

(letter references in this chart are detailed on the next page)

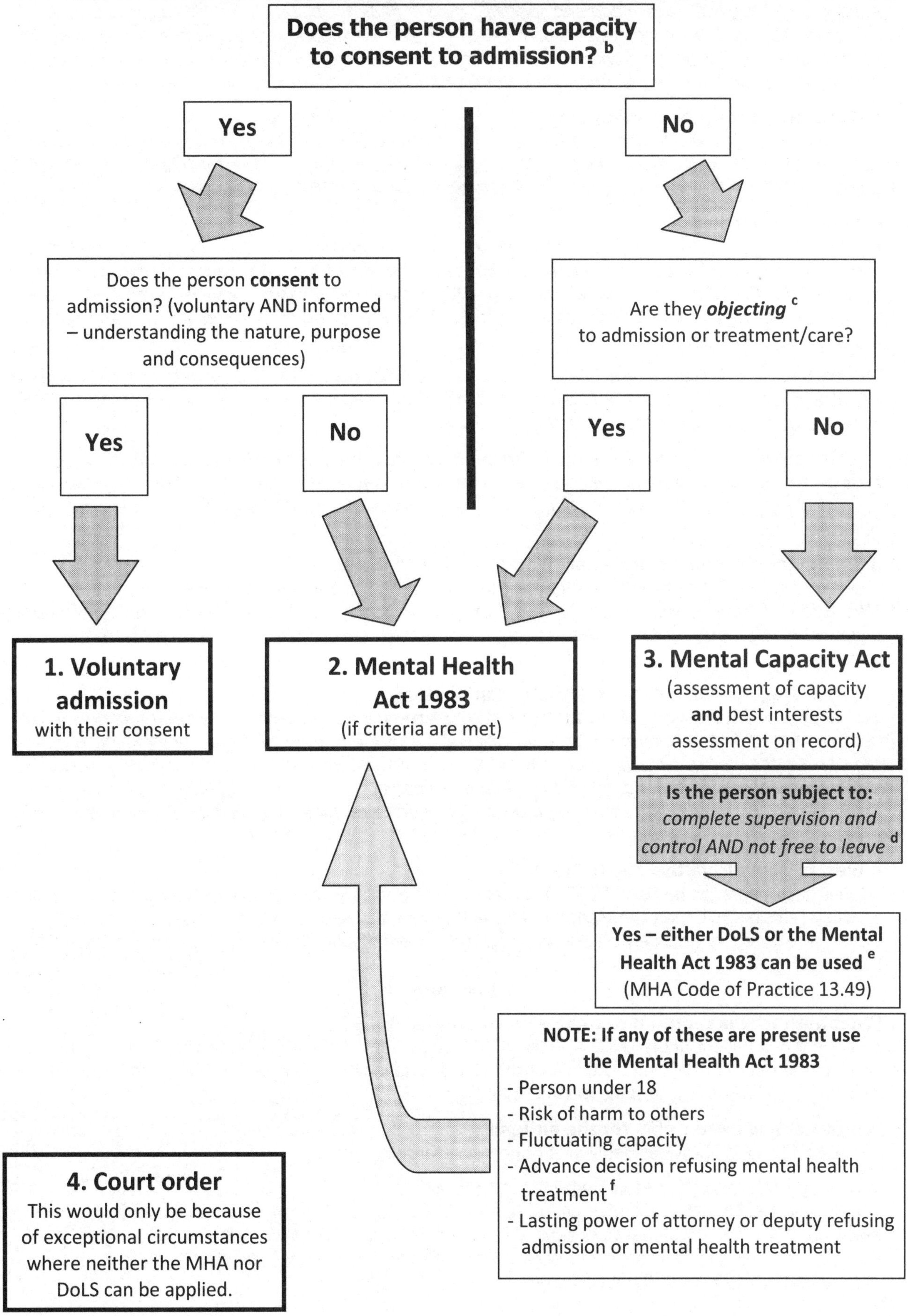

**Does the person have capacity to consent to admission? [b]**

**Yes**

Does the person **consent** to admission? (voluntary AND informed – understanding the nature, purpose and consequences)

- **Yes** → **1. Voluntary admission** with their consent
- **No** → **2. Mental Health Act 1983** (if criteria are met)

**No**

Are they ***objecting*** [c] to admission or treatment/care?

- **Yes** → **2. Mental Health Act 1983** (if criteria are met)
- **No** → **3. Mental Capacity Act** (assessment of capacity **and** best interests assessment on record)

**Is the person subject to:** *complete supervision and control AND not free to leave* [d]

**Yes – either DoLS or the Mental Health Act 1983 can be used** [e] (MHA Code of Practice 13.49)

**NOTE: If any of these are present use the Mental Health Act 1983** (→ 2. Mental Health Act 1983)

- Person under 18
- Risk of harm to others
- Fluctuating capacity
- Advance decision refusing mental health treatment [f]
- Lasting power of attorney or deputy refusing admission or mental health treatment

**4. Court order**

This would only be because of exceptional circumstances where neither the MHA nor DoLS can be applied.

**a. Treatment for mental disorder**
The Mental Health Act Code of Practice (para 24.3) states: *'In the Act, 'medical treatment' includes nursing, psychological intervention and specialist mental health habilitation, rehabilitation and care ...'* and (para 13.37): *'This may include treatment of physical conditions that is intended to alleviate or prevent a worsening of symptoms or a manifestation of the mental disorder (eg a clozapine blood test) or where the treatment is otherwise part of, or ancillary to, treatment for mental disorder.'*

**b. Capacity to consent to admission**
Case law has considered what a person needs to understand to have capacity to consent to admission to a mental health ward. The cases are: *AM v SLAM & the Secretary of State for Health [2013] UKUT 0365 (AAC)* and *A PCT v LDV, CC & B Healthcare Group [2013] EWHC 272* (see page 47).

**c. What is objecting?**
The Mental Capacity Act (Schedule 1A) states: *'In determining whether or not P objects to something, regard must be had to all the circumstances (so far as they are reasonably ascertainable), including the following - (a) P's behaviour; (b) P's wishes and feelings; (c) P's views, beliefs and values. (d) But regard is to be had to circumstances from the past only so far as it is still appropriate to have regard to them.'*

The DoLS Code of Practice (para 4.47) notes: *'...whether that objection is reasonable or not is not the issue'.* and (para 4.46): *'If there is reason to think that a person would object if able to do so, the person should be assumed to be objecting.'*

The Mental Health Act Code of Practice[20]: *'In deciding whether a patient objects to being admitted to hospital, or to some or all of the treatment they will receive there for mental disorder, decision-makers should err on the side of caution and, where in doubt, take the position that a patient is objecting.'*

**d. Complete supervision and control and not free to leave**
The Care Quality Commission[7], referring to the Supreme Court ruling in *Cheshire West,* has stated: *'The 'acid test' for a deprivation of liberty is if the person is not free to leave and is under continuous supervision. This is likely to be met for any incapacitated patient who requires psychiatric hospital admission.'*

**e. Either DoLS or the Mental Health Act can be used**
The Mental Health Act Code of Practice (para 13.58) comments: *'The choice of legal regime should never be based on a general preference for one regime or the other, or because one regime is more familiar to the decision-maker than the other ... Both regimes provide appropriate procedural safeguards to ensure the rights of the person concerned are protected during their detention. Decision-makers should not therefore proceed on the basis that one regime generally provides greater safeguards than the other.'*

**f. Electro-convulsive therapy (ECT)**
Special rules apply to the use of ECT. If a person has a valid advance decision or lasting power of attorney refusing ECT then the Mental Health Act cannot be used to override this unless the use of ECT is considered immediately necessary to save the patient's life or prevent a serious deterioration (Section 62 (1A)).

**Questions**

**What authority is required to treat a person under DoLS?**
Treatment of a patient under DoLS is either with their consent (if they have capacity to consent to the specific treatment) or through Section 4 of the Mental Capacity Act, in their best interests (if they lack capacity to consent to the specific treatment).

**Which Act has more rights for the patient?**
See page 112 which provides detailed information regarding rights.

**What if people disagree about which Act to use?**
The Mental Health Act Code of Practice (para 13.60) states: *'The most pressing concern should always be that if an individual lacks capacity to consent to the matter in question and is deprived of their liberty they should receive the safeguards afforded under either the Act or through a DoLS authorisation or a Court of Protection order.'*

**Admission to a mental health ward**

The chart on the previous page is based on the case of *AM v SLAM & the Secretary of State for Health [2013] UKUT 0365 (AAC).* The judgment by Mr Justice Charles, President of the Upper Tribunal, on appeal from an earlier Mental Health Tribunal concerned an older woman detained under Section 2. When admitting people to mental health wards Mr Justice Charles identified three key points to be addressed in the following order:

---

**1.** *'Whether the relevant person has the capacity to consent to the arrangements referred to in s. 131 MHA?'*

Note: Section 131 states a person can be admitted informally. If a person has capacity they can consent to admission and if they refuse, the Mental Health Act could be used to detain the person. If the person lacks capacity question 2 arises.

---

**2.** *'Whether the hospital might be able to rely on the provisions of the MCA to lawfully assess or treat the relevant person?'*

Note: This relates to whether the person is compliant (not objecting) to the admission and/or treatment and meets the eligibility criteria for DoLS. If the care regime on the ward is a deprivation of liberty then DoLS could be used. If the person is not compliant (objecting) or is not eligible for DoLS, the Mental Health Act applies.

---

**3.** *'How should the existence of a choice between reliance on the MHA and the MCA and its DOLS be taken into account?'*

Note: This relates to a situation where either DoLS or the MHA could be used and how staff should decide which one to use. Mr Justice Charles noted in this situation: '... *it will generally but not always be more appropriate to rely on DOLS in such circumstances ...'*

He continued that the person making the decision about whether to use DoLS or the Mental Health Act in this situation (the compliant incapacitated patient): '...*needs to consider the actual availability of the MCA regime and then compare its impact, if it was used, with the impact of detention under the MHA... This involves ...taking a fact sensitive approach, having regard to all the relevant circumstances, to the determination of the 'necessity test' and thus in the search for and identification of the least restrictive way of best achieving the proposed assessment or treatment ...'*

It is important to note that as part of this hearing Mr Justice Charles clarified that an earlier decision where he stated the Mental Health Act had 'primacy' over DoLS was misleading and that: '... *general propositions in respect of issues that arise concerning the inter-relationship between the MHA and the MCA are dangerous ...'*

---

**Community treatment orders (CTO), guardianship, conditional discharge and leave of absence**

There have been a series of rulings by the Upper Tribunal in relation to the community powers of the Mental Health Act and their relationship with DoLS. The specific rulings are listed below and practitioners are advised to consult them directly but, in summary, the rulings taken together provide the following general practice guidance:

- Being under a CTO, guardianship, conditional discharge or leave of absence do not in themselves mean a person is deprived of their liberty.
- The restrictions in a care plan for someone under a CTO, guardianship, conditional discharge or leave of absence however can mean a person is deprived of their liberty if they lack capacity to consent to the restrictions.
- CTO, guardianship, conditional discharge or leave of absence cannot authorise a deprivation of liberty.

- If a person under a CTO, guardianship, conditional discharge or leave of absence is deprived of their liberty this MUST be authorised either through DoLS (care home or hospital) or a Court of Protection order.
- DoLS can coexist with a CTO, guardianship, conditional discharge or leave of absence.
- If both are in place, staff (and the Mental Health Tribunal in case of an appeal) need to confirm that both are needed. For example, a person may present a risk of harm to himself (DoLS) and also harm to others (guardianship, CTO, conditional discharge or leave of absence).

Some cases relating to the above points are:

**CTO** – *PJ v A Local Health Board and Others [2015] UKUT 0480 (AAC)*

**Guardianship** – *NL v Hampshire CC [2014] UKUT 475 (AAC)* and *NM v Kent CC [2015] UKUT 0125 (AAC)* and *KD v A Borough Council [2015] UKUT 0251 (AAC)*

**Conditional discharge** – *Secretary of State for Justice v KC and C Partnership NHS Foundation Trust [2015] UKUT 0376 (AAC)*

---

**Case law examples of DoLS in mental health**

The following cases show how DoLS can be used in mental health services. They are summaries of actual court cases which can be downloaded from: *www.mentalhealthlaw.co.uk*

---

**Medical treatment by force**

A 55 year old woman with a significant learning disability lacked capacity about a number of healthcare decisions. She had cancer and a large tumour in her uterus which needed to be removed. Without surgery the cancer would spread leading to her death. The woman had a needle phobia and had failed to attend hospital when asked. A community nurse had spent considerable time with her but concluded she was unlikely to come to hospital willingly or remain there post operatively. Without the surgery the woman would die prematurely of what was otherwise a very treatable cancer.

The Mental Health Act only provides authority to treat mental disorder. Although some physical treatments are permitted, the MHA Code of Practice (para 13.37) notes these are limited to: '*... treatment of physical conditions that is intended to alleviate or prevent a worsening of symptoms or a manifestation of the mental disorder (eg a clozapine blood test) or where the treatment is otherwise part of, or ancillary to, treatment for mental disorder.'*

This was not the case for this woman so the use of the Mental Health Act was not possible. Due to the fact the woman was resisting treatment and lacked capacity a Court of Protection application was considered necessary. The court noted that all less restrictive alternatives had been considered but the only option was surgery and it authorised the following in her best interests:

1. Her sedation (covertly if needed) at home to take her to hospital
2. Conveying her to hospital by ambulance
3. Further sedation for the operation
4. Post-operative medication with sedative effect to keep her on the ward and also physical restraint to prevent her leaving the ward if needed
5. Deprivation of liberty during her post-operative recovery period

*DH NHS Foundation Trust v PS [2010] EWHC 1217 [Fam]*

**Community treatment orders and DoLS**

PJ was in his forties and had a diagnosis of mild learning disability and autistic spectrum disorder. He had challenging behaviour with a forensic history (actual bodily harm) which had led to extensive periods in hospital and medium secure units. His last admission was under Section 3 and he was discharged under a community treatment order in 2011 to a specialist learning disability registered care home.

The (non mandatory) conditions listed in his CTO included:

1. residing at the care home
2. abiding by the care plan

His care plan included the following restrictions:

1. fifteen minute observations when in the care home
2. escorted by staff when outside for the majority of time
3. unescorted leave of two hours per week plus two to three nights staying with his mother fortnightly. This leave had to be agreed by the responsible clinician and would be stopped if risk factors increased. PJ had asked for more leave but this had not been agreed to.
4. Alcohol usage limited to four units per week, monitored by staff breathalysing PJ on return from unescorted leave and if the limit was exceeded, his home leave would be stopped.

The Mental Health Tribunal hearing PJ's appeal against the community treatment order decided he was not deprived of his liberty. On appeal to the Upper Tribunal, the judge (Mr Justice Charles, President of the Upper Tribunal) found the original Tribunal made a mistake in their application of the Supreme Court ruling on deprivation of liberty. He stated:

*'...it is the practical situation on the ground created by a care and treatment regime, and so the practical impact on the freedom of the relevant person to act as he or she wishes, that matter when assessing whether objectively patients are deprived of their liberty...'*

*'...the MHRT overlooked that the fact that a person may have unescorted leave in the community does not mean that he is not deprived of his liberty if the leave is regulated and controlled, and he is not free to leave in the sense of removing himself permanently in order to live where and with whom he chooses.'*

*PJ v A Local Health Board and Others [2015] UKUT 0480 (AAC)*

---

## Rights and Protection: DoLS and the Mental Health Act

The question of whether DoLS or the Mental Health Act has more rights or is less restrictive is raised frequently. To clarify and resolve some of the misunderstandings that mental health staff can have about DoLS the table below provides a comparison between the two. The Mental Health Act Code of Practice (para 13.58) states: *'Both regimes are based on the need to impose as few restrictions on the liberty and autonomy of patients as possible. In the particular circumstances of an individual case, it may be apparent that one regime is likely to prove less restrictive. If so, this should be balanced against any potential benefits associated with the other regime.'* And (para 13.59): *'Both regimes provide appropriate procedural safeguards to ensure the rights of the person concerned are protected during their detention. Decision-makers should not therefore proceed on the basis that one regime generally provides greater safeguards than the other.'*

| Right or Protection | Mental Health Act | DoLS | Commentary |
|---|---|---|---|
| **Legal criteria to ensure appropriate use of the power** | Yes | Yes | Both DoLS and the Mental Health Act have rigorous legal criteria. Under DoLS for example, there is a statutory requirement to take account of the person's prior wishes, the views of family and friends (not just the nearest relative) and consider less restrictive options. The courts are clear that: *'Both the framework of the Mental Health Act 1983 and the Mental Capacity Act 2005 are rigorous in affording a regime of both protection and review.'*<br>*Northamptonshire Healthcare Trust & CCG v ML [2014] EWCOP 2* |
| **Professional assessors with additional training** | Yes | Yes | A weakness of DoLS may be inferred that it only requires two assessors however the 'extra' assessor is effectively the local authority (supervisory body) which authorises the deprivation of liberty. The assessors for both DoLS and the Mental Health Act must be professionals with additional specialist training and they are required to undertake update training each year. It is true however that Mental Health Act AMHPs undergo a more rigorous qualification course with more detailed update training. |
| **Inform person of their rights** | Yes | Yes | Both forms of detention place an initial and ongoing duty on the care provider to inform the person of their rights both verbally and in writing. In addition the provider must explain the rights in a suitable way for each person. |
| **Appeal to a court or tribunal** | Yes | Yes | Many people in mental health services would argue the Mental Health Act offers a better right of appeal via the Mental Health Tribunal. However, this is not the view of the President of the Upper Tribunal, Mr Justice Charles[21], who has said the better vehicle is the Court of Protection (for DoLS cases) as it has wider discretion in its decision making and involves a greater level of scrutiny which is required in deciding the best interests criteria for DoLS. Although the Mental Health Tribunal holds hearings quickly, it is very limited in its decision making powers and the level of evidence it requires is limited as most hearings are resolved in a matter of three hours. |
| **Review** | Yes | Yes | The Mental Health Act has a more formalised review mechanism via hospital managers' hearings however the discharge rate of such hearings is negligible calling into question their effectiveness. DoLS has a review process which involves an independent professional reassessment of one or more of the detention criteria. |

| Right or Protection | Mental Health Act | DoLS | Commentary |
|---|---|---|---|
| **Advocacy** | Yes | Yes | Both offer a right to advocacy, Independent Mental Health Advocacy (IMHA) for those detained under the Mental Health Act and Independent Mental Capacity Advocacy (IMCA) for those under DoLS. In addition under DoLS the representative has their own right to advocacy support. |
| **Independent support** | Yes | Yes | A strength of the Mental Health Act is that if a person has a nearest relative under the Act they should be consulted prior to detention under Section 2 and 3 and can object and prevent the detention taking place. In reality, however, this is a very rare event and the majority of nearest relatives do not object and can have their authority removed by the county court. The nearest relative also has a right to request the discharge of the person detained. Again, however, this is a very rare occurrence and the majority of nearest relatives never make such requests. In comparison under DoLS the representative, although not able to block detention, offers the following advantages. 1. direct right of appeal to the Court of Protection 2. right to request a review 3. if the person has capacity in the matter they can choose their own representative 4. a duty to visit the person on a regular basis 5. a specific duty as part of the role to support the person detained. |
| **Monitoring** | Yes | Yes | The Care Quality Commission has specific legal duties to monitor DoLS and the Mental Health Act and produces separate annual reports on both. At present its inspection of those under the Mental Health Act is more rigorous when the detail and content of those annual reports are compared. |
| **Proportionate initial duration** | No | Yes | The maximum duration of each standard DoLS is determined by the BIA based on the person's history, condition and specific circumstances. The Mental Health Act applies a standard time period to detention irrespective of a person's specific circumstances. Although under both the person may be discharged earlier. |
| **Refusal of treatment** | No | Yes | A person under DoLS retains the right (if they have capacity) to refuse any treatment. If they lack capacity it can only be given if the legal criteria of best interests are met. The Mental Health Act does include this right and people detained under Section 2 or 3 can immediately be treated (by force if necessary) for mental disorder whether or not they have capacity and whether or not they consent. Such treatment under the Mental Health Act is also not subject to the protection of the best interests assessment under the MCA. |
| **Copies of Assessments** | No | Yes | Under DoLS, copies of all assessments must legally be given to the person concerned and also their representative therefore providing a person with the evidence for their detention. This is not the case with the Mental Health Act where people have to make a request for copies themselves relying on the guidance in the Code of Practice. |

**Note:** A practical issue at the time of writing (October 2015) relates to the current backlog of DoLS assessments around the country. Although a person has more or less equal rights under both powers, if there is a backlog of DoLS assessments in an area that means a person will not get assessed quickly for DoLS then effectively the Mental Health Act offers more rights and protection simply because it is actually available. A person waiting several weeks for a DoLS assessment is without the DoLS rights listed above for that time.

## Safeguarding Adults and DoLS

The Care Act 2014 created a statutory duty on local authorities to make enquiries, or ask others to make them, when they think an adult with care and support needs may be at risk of abuse or neglect. The Act does not however provide any legal authority or powers to then take action to safeguard the adult. Some actions that are taken to safeguard an adult from coming to harm can result in a deprivation of liberty if that person lacks capacity. A lack of capacity to make decisions often makes people vulnerable and increases the likelihood of safeguarding issues arising. The case law in this area indicates that many local authorities and social care staff are not aware of the statutory limitations of safeguarding adults. The Association of Directors of Adult Social Services (ADASS) and the Local Government Association (LGA) have highlighted the importance of ensuring safeguarding policies are MCA compliant [22] and staff involved in safeguarding are trained on the Act.

---

**Restricting contact with families where abuse is suspected**

A recurring theme of case law relates to safeguarding actions taken where family abuse is suspected with regard to a person lacking capacity. Although safeguarding adults provides a framework for investigating such concerns it does not provide authority to take any action to restrict contact with family or remove a person from their family. These actions either require consent from the adult concerned or, if the person lacks capacity, the authority of the Mental Capacity Act and the Court of Protection.

When contact with family is restricted (supervised or prevented) and they object the involvement of the Court of Protection is required. This is because these actions also create a breach of Article 8 (private and family life) of the European Convention on Human Rights and this requires authority from a court. In these circumstances DoLS does not provide sufficient authority, as although it can authorise deprivation of liberty, it does not permit interference of Article 8. The case of Steven Neary (see page 103) is highly instructive in relation to this.

---

**Examples from case law**

There are unfortunately too many cases to list in relation to local authorities being taken to court regarding their failure to use the Mental Capacity Act (and DoLS) when safeguarding adults. Local authorities may consider they are acting in *'good faith'* to protect a vulnerable adult or have a *'duty of care'* to protect a person but as the cases below hopefully highlight, this is not adequate in law and can and does result in legal claims against local authorities. The central lesson for local authority staff is that when an action is taken to safeguard an adult, they must ask themselves what legal authority is being used. For people aged 16 and over who lack capacity the legal authority required in most cases is the Mental Capacity Act.

**Milton Keynes Council v RR [2014] EWCOP B19**

This case involved an older woman with dementia living with her son who provided care in the home. Several safeguarding alerts had been raised due to unexplained bruising and cuts to the woman's face. Following another such report, local authority staff visited the woman at home while her son was out. The woman was unable to explain the cuts and bruises and given their concerns about the situation and her vulnerability the local authority staff decided she should be taken to a care home pending a safeguarding investigation. The local authority staff recorded that the woman *'willingly left her home'.* The staff knew the son would object to his mother being removed but since he was not present they removed her.

The son subsequently sued the local authority and won the case. The judge delivered a strong rebuke to the council as follows: *'The way they have dealt with this case has been woefully inadequate from the start. It has resulted in avoidable and unlawful interference in respect of RR's Art. 5 right to liberty and security of person and her Art. 8 right to respect for her private and family life and her home. Those rights are not invalidated, nor are the unlawful interferences with those rights rendered any less serious by virtue of RR's incapacity.'*

What should local authority staff have done?

To move an adult (in this situation) would require either their consent or the use of the Mental Capacity Act. The woman was clearly confused and although it was recorded that she *'willingly left her home'* the judge considered the evidence indicated she lacked capacity to make this decision. Once a person is assessed as lacking capacity the use of the Mental Capacity Act would need to be recorded by professionals. This would have been enough if none of the woman's family objected to the move, however it was clear the son would object. In this situation an emergency application to the Court of Protection to remove her was needed. The Court of Protection can be approached 24 hours a day and judges are available to make emergency orders at any time of day or night.

Milton Keynes failed to apply to the Court of Protection for an emergency order to remove the woman and also failed to recognise the woman would be deprived of her liberty in the care home where she was placed. Only after 19 days in the care home did the local authority apply to the court. The failure to apply the Mental Capacity Act resulted in breaches of the woman and her son's human rights.

**Essex County Council v RF & Others [2015] EWCOP 1**

This case involved a 91 year old man who had lived alone for the previous 15 years. He had dementia and other physical health problems. In May 2013 safeguarding concerns were raised by the man's friends from church about his financial vulnerability and risk of exploitation. The local authority investigated and in addition to the concerns raised by his friends they became concerned about the man's ability to self-care in his home. Following another call from a friend, the local authority became very concerned about his safety and visited again. The social worker involved *'persuaded'* the man he needed to go to a care home allegedly by saying it was a hotel and then saying she would call the police if he did not comply. Although he was described as *'very reluctant'* to leave and distressed the social worker recorded this as a *'voluntary'* admission to the care home.

Despite the man's continued expressed wish to leave the care home a standard DoLS authorisation was not put into place until two months after his admission. His family supported the care home placement but his church friends opposed it. His friends wrote to the Court of Protection expressing their concerns and this resulted in further in investigation by the court. The judge found the local authorities actions in moving the man were unlawful and ordered the local authority to pay him damages of £60,000 plus his legal costs of approximately £50-64,000 plus the care homes fees paid to date of between £23-25,000.

The judge stated: *'The protection for the individual enshrined in the MCA and the Codes of Practice was ignored by ECC'.*

The judge found the local authority had failed to:

1. consider 'less restrictive options'
2. identify and authorise DoLS
3. apply to the Court of Protection given there was a dispute about residence/best interests
4. review the DoLS or apply to the Court of Protection even though there was a dispute about the man's capacity
5. appoint an advocate (IMCA) for the man despite the fact he was objecting to being in the care home and qualified for one under DoLS.

As with the previous case, safeguarding adults does not provide any authority to move an adult. Such action (in this situation) would require either the consent of the adult or the use of the Mental Capacity Act or other law such as the Mental Health Act. Although the man in this case had dementia his capacity was not assessed at the time of the move. Despite writing his admission was 'voluntary' the evidence was that he had not consented and no assessment of capacity had been undertaken.

**Note:** Even if the man had been found to lack capacity to the move and the social worker had considered it was in his best interests to move, an emergency application to the Court of Protection would still have been needed as he was clearly objecting to leaving his home. Another option could have been a completed DoLS authorisation before attempting the move with an immediate appeal to the Court of Protection given his objections to moving. Further legal advice would be needed by a local authority in this situation.

## Children, Young People and Deprivation of Liberty

Although DoLS only applies to those aged 18 and over in care homes or hospitals, the Court of Protection can authorise deprivation of liberty for young people from the age of 16 in any placement. This is an important issue for children's social services as there have been a series of court cases involving young people in residential schools, non-secure children's homes and foster homes who lack capacity where the Court of Protection has identified a deprivation of liberty. Based on the case law the main group of young people are those with a learning disability being placed in these settings. If they lack capacity there can be restrictions that mean they are subject to complete supervision and control and not free to leave and are therefore deprived of their liberty.

The positive duty on the state under the Human Rights Act to prevent human rights breaches means it is incumbent on placing local authorities to identify those who could be deprived of their liberty and ensure the deprivation is legally authorised. A Court of Protection judge stated the following in a recent case:

*'These issues potentially affect a large number of children and young people who lack capacity but who currently reside in non-secure children's homes or residential special schools. By way of example only, as at 31st March 2014, there were more than 6,500 over 16 year olds residing in care homes, children's homes or residential special schools. The Secretary of State has not yet been able to determine the proportion of those 6,500 odd young people who may lack capacity.'*

*Liverpool City Council v SG [2014] EWCOP 10*

---

**Supreme Court ruling**

The Supreme Court ruling in Cheshire West considered the issue of restraint and deprivation in children and young people: *'All children are (or should be) subject to some level of restraint. This adjusts with their maturation and change in circumstances. If MIG and MEG had the same freedom from constraint as would any child or young person of similar age, their liberty would not be restricted, whatever their level of disability. As a matter of objective fact, however, constraints beyond those which apply to young people of full ability are and have to be applied to them. There is therefore a restriction of liberty in their cases. Because the restriction of liberty is and must remain a constant feature of their lives, the restriction amounts to a deprivation of liberty.'*

---

**Duties on local authorities**

At the time of writing (October 2015) a recent judgment has identified the key points in relation to deprivation of liberty for children and young people. In this case *A Local Authority v D & Ors [2015] EWHC 3125 (Fam)* a 14 year old child living in a children's home under an interim care order was found to be deprived of his liberty. He had a moderate to severe learning disability and was not competent to consent to his placement in the home or the restrictions placed upon him. In the home he was subject to 15 minute observations and was always escorted when outside.

The judge provided the following guidance at the end of the ruling outlining the possible methods to authorise a deprivation of liberty for children and young people:

> *'(1) Local authorities are under a duty to consider whether any children in need, or looked-after children, are, especially those in foster care or in a residential placement, subject to restrictions amounting to a deprivation of liberty.*
>
> *(2) The Cheshire West criteria must be rigorously applied to the individual circumstances of each case.*
>
> *(3) The comparison to be made is not with another child of the same age placed in foster care or in a residential home, but simply with another child of the same age.*
>
> *(4) A deprivation of liberty will be lawful if warranted under statute; for example, under s.25 of the Children Act 1989 or the Mental Health Act 1983 or under the remand provisions of LASPO 2012 or if a child has received a custodial sentence under the PCCSA 2000.*
>
> *(5) Where a child is not looked after, then an apparent deprivation of liberty may not in fact be a deprivation at all if it falls within the zone of parental responsibility exercised by his parents (see*

*Re D). The exercise of parental responsibility may amount to a valid consent, with the consequence that the second limb of Cheshire West is not met. In those circumstances, the court will not need to make any declaration as to the lawfulness of the child's deprivation of liberty.*

*(6) Where a child is a looked-after child, different considerations may apply, regardless of whether the parents consent to the deprivation of liberty.*

*(7) Where a child is the subject of an interim care order or a care order, it is extremely unlikely that a parent could consent to what would otherwise amount to a deprivation of liberty. In those circumstances, a local authority cannot consent to a deprivation of liberty.*

*(8) The local authority must first consider whether s.25 of the Children Act is applicable or appropriate in the circumstances of the individual case. This will require an analysis of (1) whether any of the regulations disapply s.25, (2) whether the intended placement is accommodation provided for the purposes of restricting liberty and, thus, secure accommodation within s.25 and (3) whether the test set out in s.25.1(a) or (b) is met.*

*(9) If it is not, then the s.100(4) leave hurdle is likely to be crossed on the basis that any unlawful deprivation of liberty is likely to constitute significant harm.'*

**Notes:** Point (9) refers to the ability of the High Court use its powers under its inherent jurisdiction (by giving a court order) to authorise a deprivation of liberty. This was the outcome in this particular case given the circumstances of the child.

Point (5) refers to the case of Re D – the full reference for this case is Re D [2015] EWHC 922 (Fam).

---

### Young people in transition

Another area the courts have highlighted is the transition between the Children Act (for a child) and the Mental Capacity Act and DoLS (for an adult) when the individual lacks capacity. Where a young person is under a care order of the Children Act that is due to expire it is possible to apply to the Court of Protection before the expiry date so that the court can authorise the transition to the Mental Capacity Act. The Mental Capacity Act can be applied from the age of 16 onwards and the Court of Protection can issue wide ranging and ongoing personal welfare orders. These could include where the young person (in their best interests) should live, what contact they should have with family, care that might lead to a deprivation of liberty and issues connected with sexual relations and contraception for example. The most frequent group of people affected appear to be those with serious learning disabilities.

It should be noted that although the Court of Protection can provide a legal 'transition' to the Mental Capacity Act before the Children Act expires, local authorities need to approach the court as early as possible so that it has time to consider the case and make a ruling.

The Mental Capacity Act Code of Practice and the Mental Health Act Code of Practice both contain chapters on children and young people.

---

### Case law examples

Below are examples of Court of Protection cases where the court has found an unlawful deprivation of liberty concerning young people.

#### C v A Local Authority & Others [2011] EWHC 1539 (Admin)

This is often referred as the *'blue room'* case because the residential school involved used a special room to manage the behaviour of the young man concerned, C, who had autism and a severe learning disability. The judge in this case found the man had been unlawfully deprived of his liberty and, although the school had initiated and enforced the restrictions listed below, it was the state body (the local authority) that placed him there that was considered responsible. The judge identified the following restrictions that meant C was deprived of his liberty:

*i.* *'If C attempts to leave the school he will be prevented or brought back and the risk of absconsion is regarded as serious and is provided for accordingly;*

*ii.* *He is closely accompanied at all times of the waking day by at least two members of staff and there are supervisory waking staff at night;*

*iii. C has no choice but to accept the complete control of the staff as to what he does and where he goes including whether he can use the garden, his bedroom or the splash room;*

*iv. All of the doors to the outside of C's corridor are locked and the majority of doors within his accommodation are capable of being locked and from time to time are locked in the circumstance that C is not able to unlock the doors;*

*v. C's only access to the community is when that is organised for him and when sufficient staff are available;*

*vi. C is subject to repeated daily restraints and seclusions in the blue room;*

*vii. C has no control over the use of his accommodation by others.'*

*'The balance of evidence is clear that C needs a placement which now and for the foreseeable future will involve physical and systemic restrictions that amount to a deprivation of liberty and that this is justified by his extreme vulnerability, his complex needs including his severe learning disability and aggressive behaviours and his propensity to abscond.'*

It should be noted that this ruling was before the Supreme Court's decision in *Cheshire West* and fewer restrictions can lead to a deprivation of liberty to being identified today.

**Liverpool City Council v SG [2014] EWCOP 10**

This case concerned a woman (aged 19 at the time of the hearing) with a learning disability and challenging behaviour living in a children's home. The judge identified the following restrictions leading to a deprivation of her liberty:

*'... she is the subject of very considerable staffing on a 3:1 basis. The staffing includes monitoring her while she is in the bathroom (ensuring her dignity is maintained at all times), locking the front door as a preventative measure, following, observing and monitoring her on visits into the community, and if she 'attempts to leave the staff supporting her, they should follow several paces behind her and attempt to maintain conversation.' Items which may be used for self harm will be removed, and she remains supported 3:1 during the day and 2:1 during the night.'*

He continued: *'It is completely accepted by and on behalf of the local authority that that package of existing measures clearly amounts to a deprivation of her liberty as that concept has now been explained, in particular in paragraph 46 of the judgment of Baroness Hale of Richmond in the Cheshire West case ...'*

## Intensive Care Units and Hospices

Just prior to the publication of this book (end of October) the High Court released a judgment *(the Queen v HM senior coroner for inner London and Kings College Hospital NHS Foundation Trust [2015] EWHC 2990 (Fam)* looking at deprivation of liberty in an intensive care unit (ICU). The ruling supersedes previous guidance from the Law Society[11] in relation to this setting and provides guidance on the approach to be taken in the future for 'critical' care situations. We have taken ICUs and hospices together as they appear to share similarities in terms of identifying a deprivation of liberty.

The case concerned a woman with Down's syndrome who died whilst in intensive care. Although she was not under a DoLS authorisation at the time, the court was asked to consider whether given her situation she was deprived of her liberty in the ICU. It was argued that given the Supreme Court ruling and guidance from the Law Society the woman was under *'complete supervision and control and not free to leave'* in the ICU and was therefore deprived of her liberty. The judges hearing the case however both found she was NOT deprived of her liberty. The ruling indicates that the majority of people in ICU or hospices who lack capacity would not be considered to be deprived of their liberty.

Lord Justice Gross highlighted that the Supreme Court ruling in Cheshire West related to the long term *living arrangements* for three people with learning disabilities and should not be applied unmodified to other situations such as ICU or other settings. Although a person in these settings could be deprived of their liberty following the Supreme Court ruling each case must be considered on the individual circumstances.

Lord Justice Gross stated: *'...the notion that Cheshire West requires treating all patients in an ICU (and other hospital settings) for more than a very brief period as subject to a deprivation of liberty provided only that they lacked capacity to consent to the particular stage of treatment, would involve a wholesale extension rather than an application of that authority. Again with respect, any such extension would be mechanistic, unwarranted and divorced from the mischief Cheshire West was seeking to address.'*

Lord Justice Gross continued: *'...the reality was that M remained in the ICU, not because she had been detained or deprived of her liberty but because for pressing medical reasons and treatment she was unable to be elsewhere. There is no evidence whatever of a decision by the hospital other than to admit M to the ICU and to attempt life-saving treatment.'* The judge also noted that the hospital did not refuse to discharge the patient and intended to discharge her 'once safe to do so'.

Both judges in the case stated that the Law Society guidance[11] in relation to assessing whether a person was free to leave was not applicable in the ICU setting. The guidance had suggested that staff should ask themselves the hypothetical question whether if family asked to discharge a person they would be allowed to do so. Lord Justice Gross stated: *'...it is fanciful in this case to suppose that the Claimant would have sought to remove M from the hospital while she was undergoing treatment in the ICU and therefore idle to consider what the hospital's response would have been. I cannot accept that, as submitted by Ms Butler-Cole and suggested by the Law Society Practical Guide, the hospital's potential response to an unasked question – and one which could not sensibly have been asked – by itself constitutes or evidences a deprivation of liberty.'* Mr Justice Charles in relation to this point also stated: *'I do not agree that this hypothetical question needs to be put in each case. This is because it does not reflect the concrete situation on the ground. Rather its introduction has the potential for promoting and introducing controversy (a) between the treating team and caring and responsible family members, such as the Claimant in this case...'.*

What appears to be instrumental in the Judges deciding this was not a deprivation of liberty was the short period of time (less than 3 weeks) coupled with the treatment being urgent and life-saving in nature and that the woman's family where actively involved and supportive of the care and treatment she received.

In comparison, it would appear to the authors, based on this judgment that the following situations would lead to a deprivation of liberty in ICU or hospice:

1. There is a serious debate as the to the proper treatment

2. There is active resistance from family members to a particular course of treatment
3. There is active resistance from the person (lacking capacity) to the treatment
4. Family or friends ask to discharge the person and this is refused
5. A person (lacking capacity) asks to discharge themselves or physically tries to and this is refused

---

**Other factors for ICU and hospices**

Guidance from the Intensive Care Society[14] has provided additional information on when a person in ICU would not be considered to be deprived of their liberty as including those who:

'...• *have the capacity to decide to be admitted to intensive care*
• *consent to the restrictions applied to them*
• *gave consent for intensive care admission prior to losing capacity – for instance prior to surgery (though they must have had an understanding that they may be under continuous supervision and control and not free to leave at some time within their stay).'*

Moreover, the Department of Health has issued the following guidance[15]:

'... *the Department of Health does not consider a state of unconsciousness in itself as being a mental disorder. As such, we would not consider that an individual who is unconscious and who does not have a mental disorder would be eligible for a standard authorisation.'*

The Department of Health[15] has also stated:

*'One area that has caused particular concern is that of palliative care. For the purpose of this guidance, we consider palliative care to be concerned with the last few weeks of life.*

*The first thing to say here is that if a person receiving palliative care has the capacity to consent to the arrangements for their care, and does consent, then there is no deprivation of liberty. Furthermore, if the person has capacity to consent to the arrangements for their care at the time of their admission or at a time before losing capacity, and does consent, the Department considers this consent to cover the period until death and that hence there is no deprivation of liberty. (An important exception would be if the care package to which the individual consented were to change in a manner that imposed significant extra restrictions or which included care contrary to the previously expressed wishes and preferences of the individual. In such circumstances, the individual's consent is unlikely to cover the changed care and an application for a DoLS authorisation or a Court of Protection order may be required if there is or will be a deprivation of liberty.)'*

## Deprivation of Liberty in the Community

Some people confuse the Deprivation of Liberty Safeguards (DoLS); (a schedule attached to the back of the Mental Capacity Act allowing a deprivation of liberty in a hospital or care home) with a deprivation of liberty (DoL) which can occur anywhere. The legal method used to deprive a person of their liberty is partly determined by location. For example, to authorise the deprivation of liberty of a prisoner, the criminal law would be used. In a hospital or care home, a deprivation of liberty could be either under the Mental Health Act 1983 (but only if the care home is registered to use the Mental Health Act), DoLS or a court order. However, in the community outside of these settings such as supported living, a person's own home or residential schools the only option is a court order.

---

The Mental Capacity Act has more than one provision available to allow a person to be deprived of their liberty. They are as follows:

| | |
|---|---|
| DoLS (Schedule A1) | A legal process supervised and authorised by the local authority |
| Sections 16 (2) (b) & Section 4A(3) | Deprivation of liberty following a court order |
| Section 4B | Deprivation of liberty while an urgent court application is made to save a person's life or prevent serious deterioration |

There are also provisions outside of the Mental Capacity Act. The most relevant to readers of this book is the inherent jurisdiction which is a court's authority to authorise a deprivation of liberty due to vulnerability (ie coercion) by giving a court order.

---

### Community Mental Health Act Provisions

Guardianship, Community Treatment Orders, Conditional Discharge and Section 17 leave are all provisions of the Mental Health Act that mainly operate in the community. It is important to note however they do not give authority to deprive a person of their liberty.

---

### The Streamlined Procedure

In 2014, a streamlined Court of Protection procedure was created to make it easier to apply for and obtain court orders authorising a deprivation of liberty in the community. This meant that orders could be obtained without a court hearing by a judge checking all the paperwork submitted. Some controversy surrounded this procedure and in particular the issue of whether the person (lacking capacity) who was the subject of the court order should be joined as a party (being a 'party' in legal proceedings means that the person has greater rights in terms of their involvement). After a number of hearings, the latest position is that this procedure is still to be used to authorise a deprivation of liberty in settings outside of hospitals and care homes such as supported living or a person's own home. People often refer to this as a community DoL or judicial authorisation.

---

### Forms

A community deprivation of liberty order is requested under the streamlined procedure using a form called COPDOL10. At the time of writing the form is likely to be amended in light of the additional guidance from the judge in the case of *NRA & Ors, Re [2015] EWCOP 59*. Staff should regularly check to see whether updated forms have been made available.

It may be downloaded from: www.gov.uk/guidance/deprivation-of-liberty-orders

In order to use the streamlined procedure, evidence must be sent to the court of protection with the COPDOL10 form. This evidence must include (but is not limited to) the following:

- Mental capacity assessment
- Best interests assessment

- Care plan
- Confirmation that the person is of 'unsound mind'
- Evidence about the deprivation of liberty
- Consultation with the person and others close to them
- Evidence of any lasting power of attorney, deputy or advance decisions
- Confirmation that the person is not *ineligible* (see page 66)

---

**Should P be a party?**

At the time of writing, the most recent judgment *(NRA & Ors, Re [2015] EWCOP 59)* states that a person does not necessarily have to be a party to a case in which their liberty is in question. Being a 'party' in legal proceedings means that the person has greater rights in terms of their involvement. However, the judge decided that this was not practical in every case. He said that the loss of rights could be addressed through alternative methods such as the involvement of very close and concerned relatives who had often: *'..."fought P's corner" over a long time to promote his or her best interests.'* In cases where there were no friends or family the court could ask for independent witness evidence ie reports.

---

**What does this mean for local authorities?**

If a local authority identifies that someone in the community is being deprived of their liberty and they believe that this deprivation of liberty is necessary, proportionate and in the best interests of the person, they will need to apply to apply for a court order. They should do this promptly. If they believe the deprivation of liberty should not continue, they should take steps to bring it to an end by adjusting the care plan or providing more support.

Many people are concerned about the volume of cases involving a deprivation of liberty in the community however, case law has shown that scrutiny of the care plan by a judge can result in restrictions on the person being reduced in their best interests.

The case of *North Yorkshire County Council v MAG & Ors [2015] EWCOP 64,* concerned a man who was placed in a flat by the local authority. The flat was so small that he could not mobilise using his wheelchair and so used his hands and knees to crawl and drag himself up on to chairs and beds. The local authority applied for a court order to authorise the deprivation of liberty. However the Court of Protection decided that it was not appropriate to give the order as there were less restrictive options that were possible. Prior to the *Cheshire West* ruling and the requirements to obtain a court order, this type of case may never have received the benefit of independent scrutiny from a judge.

---

**Training**

For practical training courses on how to complete the COPDOL10 form designed for health and social care professionals please contact admin@edgetraining.org.uk (both authors are directors of this training company).

---

**Further Reading**

The key cases in relation to the streamlined procedure are:

X & Ors (Deprivation of Liberty) [2014] EWCOP 25
Re X (Court of Protection Practice) [2015] EWCA Civ 599
NRA & Ors, Re [2015] EWCOP 59

Available from: *www.mentalhealthlaw.co.uk*

## Care Quality Commission

The Care Quality Commission has stated[10]: *'To carry out our fundamental responsibility to protect and promote the rights of people who use health and social care, it is essential that we monitor how well care homes and hospitals understand when and how to use the Deprivation of Liberty Safeguards'.*

The CQC produces an annual report on DoLS available from: *www.cqc.org.uk.* In Wales, the Care and Social Services Inspectorate Wales and the Healthcare Inspectorate Wales also produce regular reports available from: *www.cssiw.org.uk*

---

### Notifying CQC

Regulation 18 of the *Health and Social Care Act 2008 (regulated activities) Regulations 2014* states that all care homes and hospitals must notify CQC of each Deprivation of Liberty Safeguard application and also the outcome. The CQC has reported[10] its concern that care homes and hospitals are not consistently notifying it as required: *'Around two-thirds of care homes and hospitals who make applications are failing to notify us of the applications or their outcomes, as required by Health and Social Care Act regulations.'* The CQC has a specific notification form *(statutory notification about an application to deprive a person of their liberty)* for care providers in relation to DoLS or court applications which covers both the request for DoLS and the outcome. This form can be downloaded from: *www.cqc.org.uk*

---

### Annual DoLS report

Every year the CQC produces a report on its findings in relation to the use of DoLS. In its last report[7] it made the following observation: *'The Deprivation of Liberty Safeguards are set firmly within the empowering ethos of the Mental Capacity Act (MCA). They encourage all health and social care providers to put liberty and autonomy at the heart of care planning, to avoid wherever possible the need to deprive people of their liberty'.*

---

### Authority of CQC in respect of DoLS

The CQC does not have any direct inspection or enforcement powers in relation to DoLS but it can instead take action under the Health and Social Care Act, if a care provider is not taking appropriate action in relation to DoLS.

---

### CQC inspections around DoLS

In 2014 the CQC changed its inspection methods and committed to inspect more rigorously and directly on the Mental Capacity Act and DoLS. The low threshold for DoLS introduced by the Supreme Court means that the majority of care homes and hospitals with residents who lack capacity to be resident for care will have at least one or more residents on DoLS.

In its guidance to residential care homes[23] the CQC states: *'Where it is likely that a person lacking mental capacity to consent to the arrangements to be given essential care or treatment, is deprived of their liberty, we will look for evidence that efforts have been made to reduce any restrictions on freedom, so that the person is not deprived of their liberty. Where this is not possible we will check that the deprivation of liberty has been authorised as appropriate, by use of the Deprivation of Liberty Safeguards, the Mental Health Act 1983, or by an order of the Court of Protection.'*

The official prompt for inspectors[24] during an inspection of a care provider is: *'Do staff understand the difference between lawful and unlawful restraint practices, including how to get authorisation for a deprivation of liberty?'*

Guidance on what care homes, hospitals and other care providers should consider in relation to meeting CQC standards for the operation of DoLS are given on page 97.

## Codes of Practice

The Code of Practice to the Mental Capacity Act and the supplementary Code of Practice for the Deprivation of Liberty Safeguards are designed to provide practical guidance when using the Act. They contain scenarios describing how the Act could, and should, be used. They are issued by the Lord Chancellor and approved by Parliament. Hard copies of either Code can be ordered from any bookseller and they can be downloaded free of charge as pdf files from:

*www.mentalhealthlaw.co.uk*

Given the significance of the Supreme Court ruling on deprivation of liberty, Chapter 2 of the DoLS Code of Practice called 'What is deprivation of liberty?' is no longer accurate on a number of issues. Practitioners are advised to refer to other materials such as the Supreme Court ruling itself, this handbook and the Law Society's[11] guidance. The remainder of the DoLS Code of Practice however remains accurate.

---

### Authority of the Codes

In relation to the Mental Capacity Act Code of Practice, the Supreme Court has stated the following: *'... if there is any conflict between what it says and what is said in the guidance given by the General Medical Council ... or by the British Medical Association ... then the Mental Capacity Act Code must prevail.' (Aintree Hospitals NHS Trust v James [2013] UKSC 67)*

However, Codes of Practice are not law and the legislation will always supersede the guidance given in a Code of Practice. Nevertheless the Codes of Practice can be referred to in legal proceedings and staff would need to show good reason for not following the guidance within them.

---

### Duty to 'have regard'

The following people have a legal duty to *'have regard'* to the Codes of Practice:

- health and social care professionals (doctors, nurses, social workers and others)
- paid workers (domiciliary carers, care assistants and others)
- attorneys (both enduring and lasting powers of attorney)
- deputies and researchers and independent mental capacity advocates (IMCAs)

---

### Revisions and new editions

Statutory Codes of Practice are revised from time to time by the government however this is not a frequent occurrence and a code may remain unchanged for a decade or more. At the time of writing the government has indicated that a new version of the Code of Practice for DoLS will not be released until 2018 or later to coincide with new DoLS legislation.

## DoLS Definitions

**Relative:** in relation to conflicts of interest for assessors and the appointment of representatives, a relative is defined as:

(a) a spouse, ex-spouse, civil partner or ex-civil partner
(b) a person living with the relevant person as if they were a spouse or a civil partner
(c) a parent or child
(d) a brother or sister
(e) a child of a person falling within sub-paragraphs (a), (b) or (d)
(f) a grandparent or grandchild
(g) a grandparent-in-law or grandchild-in-law
(h) an uncle or aunt
(i) a brother-in-law or sister-in-law
(j) a son-in-law or daughter-in-law
(k) a first cousin
(l) a half-brother or half-sister

Note: The relationships (c) to (k) include step relationships. References to step relationships and in-laws are to be read in accordance with Section 246 of the Civil Partnership Act 2004 (22).

*[The Mental Capacity (Deprivation of Liberty: Appointment of Relevant Person's Representative) Regulations 2008, No 1315]*

---

**Financial interests:** in relation to financial conflicts of interest, a person has a financial interest where:

(a) that person is a partner, director, other office-holder or major shareholder of the care home or hospital that has made the application for a standard authorisation

and

(b) the managing authority is a care home or independent hospital.

A major shareholder means any person holding one tenth or more of the issued shares in the care home or hospital, where the care home or hospital is a company limited by shares; and in all other cases, any of the owners of the care home or hospital.

*[The Mental Capacity (Deprivation of Liberty: Appointment of Relevant Person's Representative) Regulations 2008, No 1315]*

---

**Interested persons:** in relation to the best interests assessment, each of the following is an interested person:

(a) the relevant person's spouse or civil partner
(b) where the relevant person and another person of the opposite sex are not married to each other but are living together as husband and wife: the other person
(c) where the relevant person and another person of the same sex are not civil partners of each other but are living together as if they were civil partners: the other person
(d) the relevant person's children and step-children
(e) the relevant person's parents and step-parents
(f) the relevant person's brothers and sisters, half-brothers and half-sisters, and stepbrothers and stepsisters
(g) the relevant person's grandparents
(h) a deputy appointed for the relevant person by the court
(i) a donee of a lasting power of attorney granted by the relevant person

*[Mental Capacity Act 2005, Schedule A1]*

## DoLS Forms

The forms listed below are approved by the Department of Health and Association of Directors of Adult Social Services (ADASS) for those making DoLS applications and assessments. The forms are not statutory however which means that local authorities and others can amend or edit them for local purposes. Updated forms and guidance were released in March 2015 and can be downloaded from:

*www.adass.org.uk/mental-health-Drugs-and-Alcohol/key-documents/New-DoLS-Forms*

Although previous versions of the forms remain valid it is recommended that all care homes and hospitals destroy previous uncompleted versions of the forms. This will allow a uniform approach which may reduce confusion for DoLS assessors and other professionals.

---

**Errors on forms**

There is no provision in DoLS to correct or amend forms once they have been completed by an assessor because the forms are not statutory. We would suggest that the '*de minimis principle*' may apply in relation to errors on DoLS forms. This means an error that is too trivial to be of consequence will not invalidate the form. An example would be misspelling a person's name or address.

| Deprivation of Liberty Safeguards – Forms | | |
|---|---|---|
| **Form 1** | Request for standard authorisation and urgent authorisation | used by care homes and hospitals |
| **Form 2** | Request for a further standard authorisation | used by care homes and hospitals |
| **Form 3** | BIA combined assessments – age, mental capacity, no refusals, best interests assessments and selection of representative | used by DoLS assessors |
| **Form 4** | Mental health assessor – mental capacity, mental health and eligibility assessments | used by DoLS assessors |
| **Form 5** | Standard authorisation granted | used by local authority and Welsh health board |
| **Form 6** | Standard authorisation not granted | used by local authority and Welsh health board |
| **Form 7** | Suspension of standard authorisation | used by care homes and hospitals |
| **Form 8** | Termination of appointment as representative | used by local authority and Welsh health board |
| **Form 9** | Standard authorisation ceased | used by local authority and Welsh health board |
| **Form 10** | Review – request for and outcome of | used by care homes and hospitals and completed by local authorities and Welsh health boards |
| **Form 11** | Independent mental capacity advocate referral | used by local authority and Welsh health board |
| **Form 12** | Notification of death whilst deprived of liberty | used by care homes and hospitals |

This is an abridged and amended version of DoLS Forms 3, 4 and 5
Grey boxes provide guidance on completion of the form (and scrutiny of it)
Please note: this is not legal advice but for guidance only

## Guidance for completion and scrutiny

**DEPRIVATION OF LIBERTY SAFEGUARDS FORM 3**

**AGE, MENTAL CAPACITY, NO REFUSALS, BEST INTERESTS ASSESSMENTS AND SELECTION OF REPRESENTATIVE**

**General guidance**
*De minimis* principle – small or minor errors on forms (misspellings) will not invalidate an assessment.

Balance of probabilities – assessors can make their judgements on the 'balance of probabilities' this means what is most likely.

**What is required?** The evidence presented should be sufficient to warrant the 'deprivation of liberty' of a non-consenting adult. Mere opinion 'they lack capacity' is inadequate, there must be evidence to justify this conclusion.

**Scrutiny:** *'The responsibilities of a supervisory body ... require it to scrutinise the assessment it receives with independence and a degree of care that is appropriate to the seriousness of the decision and to the circumstances of the individual case that are or should be known to it.' London Borough of Hillingdon v Neary & Anor [2011] EWCOP 1377*

**Authorising signatories** cannot overule an assessor's conclusions but (SCIE guidance) '... *the authoriser may, and should, require further evidence if that provided appears too scanty to justify action in such a serious matter as depriving fellow citizens of their liberty.'*

**Note**: Assessors do NOT need to quote lots of case law – they need to apply it properly (for example, understand what *'complete supervision and control and not free to leave'* means and apply this).

| | | | |
|---|---|---|---|
| Full name of the person being assessed | **Conflict of interest?** If there is a potential conflict of interest for the authorising signatory when scrutinising the assessment such as prior dealings with the individual or family (general assessments or decisions, complaints, safeguarding decisions etc) they should not continue.<br>Similarly, BIAs should not have been involved with the person's care. | | |
| Date of birth<br>*(or estimated age if unknown)* | | Est. Age | |
| Name of the Assessor | **Conflict of interest?** Authorising signatories should not have a direct managerial or supervisory relationship with the BIA undertaking the assessment. The authorising signatory must: '... *approach his task as a detached supervisor.' P v Surrey CC & Surrey Downs CCG [2015] EWCOP 54* | | |

**In carrying out this assessment I have met or consulted with the following people**

| NAME | ADDRESS | CONNECTION TO PERSON BEING ASSESSED |
|---|---|---|
| | | |

**Note**: It is very important that all key professionals and family members are consulted. Even if this means a BIA has to undertake an assessment at a weekend in order to consult key people when they are available otherwise their best interests assessment will be inadequate.

**The following interested persons have not been consulted for the following reasons**

| NAME | REASON | CONNECTION TO THE PERSON BEING ASSESSED |
|---|---|---|
| | | |

Family or others should not be excluded from the consultation process because of safeguarding concerns and allegations. The courts give great weight to private and family life (Article 8 ECHR) and if someone is excluded they expect clear proven evidence and an application to the court in cases of dispute. If key family members cannot be contacted (for example because they are on holiday) a short duration DoLS may be appropriate to allow for future consultation.

**NO REFUSALS ASSESSMENT** (note: this has been moved out of order from the standard form for formatting reasons in this handbook)

| To the best of my knowledge and belief the requested Standard Authorisation <u>would not</u> conflict with an Advance Decision or a decision by a Lasting Power of Attorney, or Deputy, for Health and Welfare. | |
|---|---|

Evidence = Asking the person concerned + consulting staff + checking care records + speaking to family AND for lasting powers of attorney or deputies (where there is uncertainty such as no family to confirm details) the BIA should check the Office of the Public Guardian's register.

It is important for a BIA to explain clearly to an attorney or deputy that they are being consulted because they can refuse a DoLS authorisation if they disagree with it. The BIA should record this on the form otherwise an attorney could claim they were merely consulted about the DoLS without being told of their right to refuse.

**MENTAL CAPACITY ASSESSMENT**

**General guidance**: The assessment of capacity is NOT a clinical judgment of a person's illness but a legal assessment of whether, despite the person's impairment/disturbance of mind/brain, they have capacity to make the decision to be resident for care/treatment. While doctors may present information about a person's condition and symptoms, evidence of lacking mental capacity is required here.

The following **practicable steps** have been taken to enable and support the person to participate in the decision-making process:

Practical steps to help the person understand the information, retain it etc might include using the best time of day, a quiet room or someone the person knows and trusts. If there is a communication problem, a speech and language therapist might be appropriate.

| In my opinion the person LACKS capacity to decide whether or not they should be accommodated in this hospital or care home for the purpose of .... | |
|---|---|
| In my opinion the person HAS capacity to decide whether or not they should be accommodated in this hospital or care home for the purpose of ... | |

**Stage One**: What is the impairment of, or disturbance in the functioning of the mind or brain?

This should be the same as the mental health assessor's conclusion

**Stage Two**: Functional test

**General notes**:
*"It is inappropriate to start with a blank canvas. The person under evaluation must be presented with detailed options so that their capacity to weigh those options can be evaluated."*
*CC v KK & STCC [2012] EWHC 2136*

- Burden of proof – the burden lies with the local authority to prove a person lacks capacity. The person being assessed has to prove nothing.
- Evidence – any opinion '*They did not understand*' MUST be backed up with evidence. What the person did not understand in relation to the specific decision must be stated to show how this conclusion was reached (evidence). For example, the person may understand they are in a care home but not understand they have care needs in relation to their physical mobility.
- Good evidence records what the person says in response to questions and can illustrate that the person could not understand or use and weigh the information for example.
- A clinical description is NOT evidence of mental capacity, for example: '*they have established dementia and were confused*'.
- If a person fails one part of the assessment below, they lack capacity – it is not necessary to address all the other points. However an assessor may wish to do so as it shows they recognise a person can meet some other parts of the assessment. In borderline cases there may be some merit in recording under all headings in case of later dispute.

**a. The person is unable to understand the information relevant to the decision**
*Record how you have tested whether the person can understand the information, the questions used, how you presented the information and your findings.*

- What information (salient points) does the person need to understand? Key information given can be basic and simple: nature (what) + purpose (why) + consequences (reasonably foreseeable).
- Case law example *(Derbyshire CC v AC, EC & LC [2014] EWCOP 38)* – to have capacity to be resident for care (mental health rehabilitation unit) the person needed to understand:
  - She would live with other people (and not with her parents)
  - She would be supported by staff – care component
  - The location of the placement (near or far from family and friends)
  - The age and gender of the other residents (broadly)
  - The need to abide by house rules (this could equally be rules/restrictions of a ward)
  - Whether it was long or short term placement (living/visiting)
  - She had care needs and the risks/consequences if these needs were not met.
- What is the EVIDENCE the person does not understand the information?

**b. The person is unable to retain the information relevant to the decision**
*Record how you tested whether the person could retain the information and your findings.*

Information only needs to be retained long enough to make the decision. An inability to retain longer term information (such as the difficulties in coping at home) may affect the ability to understand risks or use or weigh information.

**c. The person is unable to use or weigh that information as part of the process of making the decision** *Record how you tested whether the person could use and weigh the information and your findings.*

A person may understand the information but not be able to use or weigh it (accept or take it into account). For example they may understand they are in a care home and what the assessor means by 'care needs' but not *accept* they have any illness or care needs. The ability to use or weigh can be affected by issues such as phobias, delusions, compulsive disorders, lack of insight. Evidence must be provided, not solely an opinion that they could not use or weigh information. Simply denying matters, being overly optimistic or changing their mind may be just a person's way of dealing with a difficult situation and does not necessarily mean they lack capacity.

**d. The person is unable to communicate their decision (whether by talking, using sign language or any other means)**
*Record your findings about whether the person can communicate the decision.*

A person who is unconscious or has 'locked in syndrome' cannot communicate but other people may be able to make a noise or blink. A description of their response to questions should be given. However the law needs the person to communicate their decision through any means.

**Stage Three**: *Explain why the person is unable to make the specific decision because of the impairment of, or disturbance in the functioning of, the mind or brain.*

An example from a BIA in practice[26]: *'Mrs Smith is unable to retain information relevant to the decision due to her memory loss and is unable to weigh information relevant due to her impaired judgment. These are both symptoms of vascular dementia, which is a permanent impairment of the brain. It is because of this impairment that she is unable to make her own decision about being accommodated at the nursing home to receive care.'*

**Note: This section has been moved forward.**
**The standard form is confusing because it starts with the best interests checklist then jumps to deprivation of liberty half way through before returning to best interests (a number of local authorities have reordered the form into the order shown here)**

| **THE PERSON IS DEPRIVED OF THEIR LIBERTY**<br>In my opinion the person is, or is to be, kept in the hospital or care home for the purpose of being given the relevant care or treatment in circumstances that deprive them of liberty **Note:** *If the answer is No then the person does not satisfy this requirement* | **YES** | |
|---|---|---|
| | **NO** | |

**The reasons for my opinion:**

**Objective**: *Applying the acid test should provide evidence of confinement in a particular restricted space for more than a negligible period of time. Refer to the descriptors in the DoLS Code of Practice in light of the acid test.*

**Information**: The sources of information used to ascertain the restrictions in place should be recorded, for example care home/hospital records, observation of the actual care/restrictions in practice, verbal information given by staff about restrictions, external sources such as family and friends and the person themselves.

**1. A list of restrictions**: (the concrete situation/evidence) These could be **a)** actual restrictions such as physical restraint **b)** what if restrictions – what would happen if the person tried to leave (note ICU case law) **c)** Restricted access – access to kitchen (locked), outside world (escort), medication (held by staff).

**2. Guzzardi**: The restrictions listed should be described in the 'Guzzardi' framework: duration, effect, manner, degree and intensity.

- Each restriction should be broken down. For example, escorted leave: How often does the person go out? How many staff go with them? How long are they allowed to be out? How far can they go? Does the person show distress being escorted or when returned? Does the person choose where to go? Are they distressed if staff are unable to escort them out? Is there evidence/risk assessment to explain the need for an escort? Is there a review process to ensure this restriction and others are monitored and kept to the minimum necessary? Have less restrictive options been tried first?

**3. Supreme Court**: Do the restrictions described above mean the person is subject to:
*'complete supervision and control AND not free to leave.*

**Note**: For restrictions relevant to Article 8 ECHR (private and family life, home and correspondence) such as restricting contact with family (because of abuse) or removing people from family (because of abuse) or opening mail, searching people, restricting access to phones, managing sexual relations – advice should be sought as Article 8 issues arise and an application to the Court of Protection may be necessary.

**Subjective:** *Evidence that the person lacks capacity to consent to being kept in the hospital or care home for the purpose of being given the relevant care or treatment.*

This could simply state 'See the assessment of mental capacity'

The placement is **imputable to the State** because:

One or more of the following answers may be appropriate (not an exhaustive list): 1) Local authority or NHS is funding part of the care package 2) Local authority or NHS placed the person in the care home/hospital 3) As a BIA, I represent the state. 4) The CQC register the care home/hospital. 5) the state became aware of the deprivation of liberty through a safeguarding referral

| **It is necessary to deprive the person of their liberty in this way in order to prevent harm to the person.** The reasons for my opinion are: | **YES** / **NO** |
|---|---|

*Describe the risks of harm to the person that could arise which make the deprivation of liberty necessary. Support this with examples and dates where possible. Include severity of any actual harm and the likelihood of this happening again.*

- What harm would the person be exposed to if they were to return home?
- What harm would arise if they did not receive care and treatment?

Harm could include physical harm, risk of exploitation or deterioration of mental or physical health. Actual examples of harm that have occurred in the past can be given here.

| **Depriving the person of their liberty in this way is a proportionate response to the likelihood that the person will otherwise suffer harm and to the seriousness of that harm.** The reasons for my opinion are: | **YES** / **NO** |
|---|---|

*With reference to the risks of harm described above explain why deprivation of liberty is justified. Detail how likely it is that harm will arise (i.e. is the level of risk sufficient to justify a step as serious as depriving a person of liberty?). Why is there no less restrictive option? What else has been explored?*

Evidence should be provided showing the likelihood of the risk (stated above) occurring and also detailing less restrictive options which have been tried unsuccessfully.

If there is a question over how appropriate a placement is but there is no other placement immediately available, it is possible to authorise a standard DoLS for a short duration whilst a new placement (or change to the current placement) is arranged. In the case of *P v Surrey CC & Surrey Downs CCG [2015] EWCOP 54* the judge stated: *'The [supervisory body] had the duty to investigate whether a less restrictive alternative was available ... It already knew that the care home was not suitable in the medium or longer term because it had been told so by the social worker undertaking the best interests assessment.'*

*North Yorkshire County Council v MAG & Ors [2015] EWCOP 64.* The judge felt that the local authority had not adequately explored less restrictive options and given that the case involved a deprivation of liberty stated: *'This is a question of MAG's liberty and I do not accept that I can authorise the deprivation of that liberty on the basis that nothing else is available. He has been in this unsatisfactory situation for a prolonged period. NYCC has been extremely slow to accept its responsibilities in relation to rehousing him.'* Given this, the judge refused to authorise the continued deprivation of liberty of the man involved. Note: this was a community deprivation of liberty case.

**BEST INTERESTS ASSESSMENT**

MATTERS THAT I HAVE CONSIDERED AND TAKEN INTO ACCOUNT

**NOTE: other rows here deleted as simply tick boxes**

BACKGROUND INFORMATION

*Background and historical information relating to the current or potential deprivation of liberty.*
*For a review look at previous conditions and include comments on previous conditions set.*

- This is equivalent to the requirement to consider all 'relevant circumstances' in the best interests checklist of the Act (Section 4). It can refer to care needs assessments, risk assessments, a brief history, diagnosis, prognosis, emotional factors, social factors, clinical opinion, funding (or lack of it) etc.
- It should not be written as a life story but present key relevant information.
- Note: this is not a community care assessment – however such an assessment can be attached as part of the relevant circumstances.

VIEWS OF THE RELEVANT PERSON

*Provide details of their past and present wishes, values, beliefs and matters they would consider if able to do so:*

**Past wishes** – Even if there are no known past wishes this must be recorded and explained.

**Present wishes** – Even if the person cannot give any views this should be noted and what the BIA did to assess any possible wishes, for example sit with the person for a period of time to see whether they were settled in the care home or hospital.

**Religious or cultural beliefs** should be recorded – if there are none this should also be recorded.

Case law – The closer a person is to having capacity the greater weight should be given to their stated views. The strength and consistency of those views is also relevant *(ITW v Z & M [2009] EWHC 2525).*

If a person is clearly objecting to the placement this would also require an immediate appeal to the Court of Protection and the best interests assessor MUST inform the local authority accordingly.

VIEWS OF OTHERS

This includes family and friends. There is no hierarchy in family or friends. What family and others said must be recorded (not just that they were consulted). This does not have to be a verbatim account but an appropriate summary with some verbatim quotes which could provide useful evidence. More information should be recorded about the views of family or friends who are close to the person concerned. If any close family or friends are recorded as objecting to the placement this requires immediate action by an application to the Court of Protection (even where the family are abusive and the placement is keeping the person safe). Legal advice should be sought (Article 8 ECHR private and family life).

| **This is in the person's best interests.**<br>**Note:** *You should consider Section 4 of the Mental Capacity Act 2005, the additional factors referred to in paragraph 4.61 of the Deprivation of Liberty Safeguards Code of Practice and all other relevant circumstances. Remember that the purpose of the person's deprivation of liberty must be to give them care or treatment.* | **YES** | |
|---|---|---|
| | **NO** | |

The reasons for my opinion are:

Relevant circumstances + person's wishes + views of others already recorded above so this section should include the following:

1. Less restrictive options – what other less restrictive options are available? What has been tried and failed? The least restrictive option does not have to be chosen. The final decision is what overall is in the person's best interests.

2. The likelihood of the person regaining capacity and, if it is a possibility, whether the BIA could wait to reassess them.

3. The manner in which the person concerned was involved in the best interests decision making process.

4. The decision was not based solely on age, appearance, behaviour or condition (although these may well have been considered under relevant circumstances).

The weight or significance of different parts (wishes, relevant circumstances, less restrictive options, risk) will vary between people and this needs to be noted as it will explain the final decision made.

If a placement is not 'ideal' but there is no immediate alternative placement, the DoLS can be authorised for a short duration with a recommendation that the person be moved as soon as possible. It would effectively be in the person's best interests to stay in the placement because any immediate alternative available is less appropriate. However, this must be balanced against the harm or risk to the person of remaining in an inappropriate placement. See 'a proportionate response' earlier. BIAs cannot force local authorities to provide certain options however evidencing less restrictive options even if not currently offered by the local authority could provide assistance in case of future court applications or be persuasive for the local authority. It would also evidence that the BIA had properly considered less restrictive options.

**BEST INTERESTS REQUIREMENT IS NOT MET**
*This section must be completed if you decided that the best interests requirement is not met.*

A Safeguarding Adult enquiry must be considered for any unauthorised deprivation of liberty. Please place a cross in the box if a referral has been made.

Date of Referral:

*Please offer any suggestions that may be beneficial to the Safeguarding Adult process, commissioners and / or providers of services in deciding on their future actions or any others involved in the resolution process.*

Case law has said if a person is deprived of their liberty but they are NOT in an appropriate placement a DoLS can be authorised for a short time whilst arrangements are made to move the person. If not authorised the local authority must be able to take immediate action to change the situation otherwise they face a claim for an unlawful deprivation of liberty *(A County Council v MB [2010] EWHC 2508).* However see 'a proportionate response' earlier for further case law.

**BEST INTERESTS REQUIREMENT IS MET**
*The maximum authorisation period must not exceed one year*

In my opinion, the maximum period it is appropriate for the person to be deprived of liberty under this Standard Authorisation is:

Authorising signatories can REDUCE the time period suggested. They cannot however extend the period beyond that stated by the BIA. Note: Recent case law *P v Surrey CC & Surrey Downs CCG [2015] EWCOP 54* where the judge was critical of a duration of ten months given by the authorising signatory when the family, advocate and BIA had concerns about the current placement and believed a move to another placement was required.

The reasons for choosing this period of time are: *Please explain your reason(s)*

The reasons should be based on the history of the person concerned, their prognosis or the expected progression of their illness and the potential effect of treatment. DoLS Code of Practice: '*... for the maximum 12-month period to apply, the assessor will need to be confident that there is unlikely to be a change in the person's circumstances that would affect the authorisation within that timescale.*'

**RECOMMENDATIONS AS TO CONDITIONS (Not applicable for review)**
Choose ONE option only

The authorising signatory can agree to or remove any conditions suggested by the BIA. They can also add their own conditions. If conditions suggested by the BIA are removed, the authorising signatory should consult them as it may affect their assessment of best interests (see statement below).

I recommend that any Standard Authorisation should be subject to the following conditions

1. Conditions are placed on the care home or hospital and they should be SMART (not a legal requirement)

   **S**pecific – clear to the staff of the care home or hospital
   **M**easurable – in order that they can be monitored
   **A**chievable – the care home or hospital is responsible for them
   **R**elevant – directly related to the DOLS itself (see Code of Practice)
   **T**ime specific – to complied with in a certain time or specify an ongoing requirement

   If this is a request for a further DoLS authorisation, the BIA should check whether any previous conditions have been followed. If they have not, this should be questioned and any new conditions should reflect the outcome of their investigation.

**SHOULD ANY RECOMMENDED CONDITIONS NOT BE IMPOSED:**

I would like to be consulted again, since this may affect some of the other conclusions that I have reached in my assessment.

| **RECOMMENDATIONS, ACTIONS AND / OR OBSERVATIONS FOR CARE MANAGER / SOCIAL WORKER / COMMISSIONER / HEALTH PROFESSIONAL** |
|---|
| This allows the BIA to make recommendations to the local authority. For example '*A social worker should be allocated to this case to the review care plan*' or '*An IMCA should be appointed to support the person and their representative*' or '*The person is objecting (verbally or physically) so an appeal to the Court of Protection should be made*'. A system should be in place to check these recommendations are followed. |

| **SELECTION OF REPRESENTATIVE** – *place a cross in one box* | |
|---|---|
| A signatory does not have to appoint the person recommended by the BIA but someone must be appointed as representative as they are a central safeguard in DoLS. | |
| I have selected and recommend that the Supervisory Body appoints the representative identified below. In so doing I confirm that: | |
| The representative **must** be someone who will appeal if the person under DoLS objects (either verbally or physically) to their placement (*AJ v A Local Authority [2015] EWCOP 5)*. If they will not do this they should not be appointed. If a family member is being proposed by a BIA they must show evidence of why they believe the person would challenge the DoLS authorisation in the Court of Protection if the person concerned was objecting (verbally or physically). In addition a representative must not have any conflicts of interest (financial or employment) and be willing to take on the role and be able to meet the person regularly. | |
| **If you are not able to name a representative please place a cross in the box and record your reason below** | |

## DEPRIVATION OF LIBERTY SAFEGUARDS FORM 4

### MENTAL CAPACITY, MENTAL HEALTH, and ELIGIBILITY ASSESSMENTS

| **MENTAL HEALTH ASSESSMENT** | |
|---|---|
| In my opinion the person IS suffering from a mental disorder within the meaning of the Mental Health Act 1983 (disregarding any exclusion for persons with learning disability). *Provide a rationale for your opinion, including details of their symptoms, diagnosis and behaviour* | |
| The assessor needs to give a clear description of the signs, symptoms and behaviour of the individual. This should provide sufficient evidence to conclude the person has a mental disorder. Guidance on conditions that meet the criteria for mental disorder are in chapter 2 of the Mental Health Act Code of Practice. | |
| In my opinion, the person's mental health and wellbeing is likely to be affected by being deprived of liberty in the following ways: | |
| This should state the effect on the person concerned of being deprived of their liberty (in the care home or hospital). For example, depression or sense of loss from no longer living in their own home or an improvement in their mental and physical health due to their care needs being met at the appropriate level. | |

**Eligibility Assessment**

See the chapter on Eligibility earlier in this book.

## DEPRIVATION OF LIBERTY SAFEGUARDS FORM 5

### STANDARD AUTHORISATION GRANTED

**THE SUPERVISORY BODY'S DECISION**

**The reasons for this period are:**

Explain with evidence from the BIA assessment. Ensure the evidence used is not selective to suit a desired outcome from the perspective of the local authority. It should be a fair summary of the reasons given and show scrutiny. The time period should not be based on the need to avoid further assessments in the interests of the local authority.
See case: *P v Surrey CC & Surrey Downs CCG [2015] EWCOP 54*

*(The period specified must not exceed the maximum period specified in the best interests assessment)*

**THE PURPOSE OF THE AUTHORISATION *is to enable the following care or treatment to be given in the hospital or care home.***

A brief description of the care being delivered, or due to be delivered, should be given here.

**The authorisation is granted because the Supervisory Body has received written copies of all required assessments and concludes each qualifying requirement is met for the following reasons.**

**EVIDENCE OF SUPERVISORY BODY SCRUTINY**

*The authoriser should indicate why they concur with the conclusions of the assessors reports and demonstrate overall scrutiny of the process:*

For authorising signatories the key issue is that they read the assessments and consider whether sufficient evidence has been presented based on a good knowledge of the legislation and case law. The authorising signatory must feel confident that the assessor has applied knowledge of the legislation and up to date case law.

Confirm that you have read and considered the assessments and believe the evidence presented meets the statutory requirements. Any actions such as speaking to the BIA or requesting further information should be recorded. Highlight elements of the assessments/evidence that you consider were particularly important in concluding the assessments met all the DoLS criteria.

| Signed *(on behalf of the Supervisory Body)* | Signature | |
|---|---|---|

Deprivation of Liberty Safeguards (DoLS)

## Rights leaflet for people on a standard DoLS

*Please note: There is not a statutory rights leaflet for people on a standard DoLS. This leaflet aims to give the main information a person should be informed about. Care home and hospital staff have a duty not only to give written information but also to explain it to the person and to take practicable steps to ensure the person understands their rights. You can download this leaflet from: www.bookswise.org.uk. There is a Department of Health leaflet called 'DoLS and You' that can also be used which contains some information on about rights.*

| Person's name | | | |
|---|---|---|---|
| Name of care home or hospital | | | |
| Date DoLS started | | Date DoLS ends | |

**What is this leaflet?**
This leaflet tells you about being on a standard DoLS and your rights. The care home (or hospital) staff have a duty to give you this information and try to explain what it means.

**Why am I on a standard DoLS?**
Two people (a doctor and a health or social care professional called a best interests assessor) have met you and assessed that your health condition has affected your ability to decide where to live. After talking to you and people who know you and considering other information they have decided it is in your best interests to stay in this care home (or hospital) to receive the care or treatment that you need.

While you are staying here there are some rules in your care plan which help to keep you safe. These rules mean you are not free to come and go as you may wish and that staff need to support and supervise you in different ways to look after you and keep you safe. This is why your local council has placed you under the protection of a standard DoLS while you are here to make sure the care home or hospital are looking after you properly.

You must be given a copy of the assessments completed by the doctor and best interests assessor giving the reason why you are on a standard DoLS and a copy of the DoLS itself from the council. Your representative (see below) will also be given a copy of these.

**How long will the DoLS last for?**
The date when your standard DoLS ends is given at the top of this leaflet. You must not leave before this time unless the care home or hospital staff say you can. If you try to leave, the staff can stop you, and if you do leave, you can be brought back.

Before the DoLS ends you should be told whether you are going to be assessed again to see if it needs to be continued for a further period of time.

**What care and treatment will I be given?**
If you can make decisions about your care and treatment then you can say yes or no to anything that is offered to you. If you lack capacity to decide then staff must assess what is in your best interests under the Mental Capacity Act. You must be involved in any such decisions and your views and wishes taken into account. Your family and other people who know you must also be consulted.

**Reviews**
If you are not happy being on a standard DoLS or think it is wrong you can, at any time, ask for a 'review'. To do this, you need to contact the local council DoLS team. A review means you will be seen by a DoLS assessor from outside the care home or hospital. This could be the same person who assessed you originally. You can write or call the council DoLS team at:

| |
|---|
| |

You can ask a member of staff to help you contact them. Your representative can also ask for a review.

**Can I appeal?**
Yes. You can appeal to the Court of Protection at any time using a special form called COPDLA. If you want to apply to the court you should write to:

Court of Protection, PO Box 70185, First Avenue House, 42-49 High Holborn, London WC1A 9JA

Telephone: 0300 456 4600 Email: courtofprotectionenquiries@hmcts.gsi.gov.uk

You can ask your representative or an independent mental capacity advocate (IMCA) to help you write to the court. Your representative can also appeal to the court themselves.

**Help from an independent advocate (IMCA)**
You are entitled to free help from an independent advocate if you want it. They can help you get information about your care and treatment, why you are being kept in a care home or hospital, what it means and what your rights are. They can also help you with appealing to the Court of Protection or asking for a review.

If you want an advocate contact your local council DoLS team (details above). If you do not want to contact the DoLS team yourself, you can ask a member of staff to contact them for you. You can also ask your representative to do this for you.

**Your representative**
Everyone under a standard DoLS has a person called a representative appointed for them. They can be a member of your family, a friend or someone such as an advocate. They are independent of the care home or hospital and they must support you as long as you are on a standard DoLS. They can ask for a review or appeal to the Court of Protection. They must come and see you regularly.

You may have chosen the representative yourself, otherwise they will have been chosen for you. Your representative for DoLS is:

If you do not want this person to be your representative speak to the local council DoLS team or ask the staff at the care home or hospital to do this for you.

**Code of Practice**
There is a legal Code of Practice that gives advice to staff in the care home or hospital about DoLS. The staff have to consider what the Code says when they take decisions about your care. You can ask to see a copy of the Code, if you want.

**How do I complain?**
If you want to complain about anything to do with your care or treatment in the care home or hospital, please speak to a member of staff. They may be able to sort the matter out. They can also give you information about the care home or hospital's complaints procedure and about any other people who can help you make a complaint, such as an advocate (see above).

If you do not feel that the care home or hospital complaints procedure can help you, contact the local council DoLS team (see details above). The Care Quality Commission (CQC) may be able to help. Contact them on telephone: 03000 616161 or email: enquiries@cqc.org.uk

## Jargon Buster

For those not familiar with DoLS there are a lot of different names, titles and terms used. A brief summary is given below:

---

**Approved Mental Health Professional (AMHP):** a health or social care professional who is approved to undertake assessments under the Mental Health Act 1983. Many AMHPs are also BIA qualified and can undertake certain assessments under DoLS.

**Authorisations:** the authority to legally hold someone in a care home or hospital under DoLS. There are two types: urgent and standard authorisations (see pages 30 and 33).

**Authorising signatory:** see 'Signatory' below (see page 93).

**Best Interests Assessor (BIA):** a health or social care professional (nurse, social worker, occupational therapist or psychologist) with an additional qualification to undertake some of the DoLS assessments (see page 91).

**Care and Social Services Inspectorate Wales and Healthcare Inspectorate Wales:** the inspectorate bodies for care homes and hospitals in Wales. They have specific responsibility for monitoring DoLS (see page 123).

**Care Quality Commission (CQC):** the inspectorate body for care homes and hospitals in England. It has specific responsibility for monitoring DoLS (see page 123).

**Court of Protection:** the court that governs the Mental Capacity Act including DoLS. It can make decisions regarding a person's mental capacity and what is in their best interests (see page 84).

**Deprivation of Liberty:** the term used in Article 5 of the European Convention on Human Rights which states that everyone has the right to liberty and it can only be taken away in certain circumstances and only if legal processes are used. It is also the term used if the Court of Protection authorises the detention of a person outside a care home or hospital. It is sometimes referred to by the acronym DoL (rather than DoLS).

**Deprivation of Liberty Safeguards:** the legislation in England and Wales (part of the Mental Capacity Act 2005) that provides the procedures and rules governing a deprivation of liberty in care homes or hospitals.

**Independent Mental Capacity Advocate (IMCA):** an independent advocate for people who lack capacity who can support and represent their views as far as possible (see page 79).

**Managing authority:** a care home or hospital (see page 97).

**Mental Health Assessor:** a doctor qualified to undertake some DoLS assessments (see page 91).

**Qualifying requirements:** a person must meet a series of requirements (legal criteria) to be placed under a standard DoLS authorisation (see page 37).

**Representative:** everyone under a standard DoLS authorisation has an independent representative appointed to support them (see page 75).

**Review:** a person under a standard DoLS authorisation has the right to a review of the decision to hold them in a care home or hospital. For example the person may ask for a review because they believe that they have regained their mental capacity regarding care and treatment (see page 82).

**Signatory:** a senior manager of a local authority (or Welsh health board) responsible for checking completed assessments from DoLS assessors and granting standard DoLS authorisations based on these (see page 93).

**Supervisory body:** a local authority or a Welsh health board (see page 93).

## DoLS – Self Assessment Quiz

1. How is restraint defined in the Mental Capacity Act?
2. What criteria must be met to restrain a person?
3. When the capacity assessment is undertaken does the assessor need to be 100% sure the person lacks capacity?
4. The best interests assessment under DoLS has four elements – name them.
5. Name five elements of the statutory best interests 'checklist' under Section 4 of the Mental Capacity Act.
6. Who is responsible for complying with any conditions attached to a standard DoLS authorisation?
7. If a family member objects to a DoLS authorisation can you appoint them as a representative?
8. To appoint a person as a representative they have to meet certain criteria – what are they?
9. Name four triggers that mean a person should get an IMCA (advocate) under DoLS.
10. Name three ways in which a review may be triggered? What is the role of a BIA in a review?
11. A person under a standard DoLS authorisation is given rights and legal protection – name four types of protection and rights for a person under DoLS.
12. Can a lasting power of attorney or deputy (with personal welfare authority) authorise the deprivation of liberty of a person?
13. The authorising signatory of a local authority is able to change three elements of a BIAs recommendations – what are they?
14. What is meant by the 'Acid Test'?
15. When can DoLS and the Mental Health Act 1983 be used simultaneously?
16. In what circumstances would a standard DoLS authorisation be suspended?
17. What are the six assessments for a standard DoLS authorisation?

The answers to the quiz can be found at *www.bookswise.org.uk* under the DoLS section.

# References


1. Alistair Burt, Minister of State for Community and Social Care, House of Commons debate, 17 June 2015, Deprivation of Liberty Safeguards Assessments (Volume 597, Part No. 18)

2. Health & Social Care Information Centre, *Mental Capacity Act (2005) Deprivation of Liberty Safeguards (England) Annual Report*, 2014-15. www.hscic.gov.uk

3. HM Government, *Valuing every voice, respecting every right: making the case for the Mental Capacity Act* , The Government's response to the House of Lords Select Committee Report on the Mental Capacity Act 2005 (June 2014)

4. Law Commission, *Consultation Paper No 222, Mental Capacity and Deprivation of Liberty, A Consultation Paper*, ISBN 9780108561634, www.lawcom.gov.uk

5. Supreme Court, *P v Cheshire West & Chester Council, P & Q v Surrey CC [2014] UKSC 19*, www.bailii.org

6. National Institute for Health Research, School for Social Care Research, *The Deprivation of Liberty Safeguards: their impact on care practice (2014)*, www.sscr.nihr.ac.uk

7. Care Quality Commission, *Monitoring the use of the Mental Capacity Act Deprivation of Liberty Safeguards in 2013/14*, www.cqc.org.uk

8. Care & Social Services Inspectorate Wales and the Healthcare Inspectorate Wales, *A national review of the use of deprivation of liberty safeguards (DoLS) in Wales*, April-May 2014, ISBN 9781473424180 www.cssiw.org.uk and www.hiw.org.uk

9. Care Quality Commission, *The state of health care and adult social care in England 2014/15*, October 2015, ISBN 9781474124935, www.cqc.org.uk

10. Care Quality Commission, *Monitoring the use of the Mental Capacity Act Deprivation of Liberty Safeguards in 2012/13*, www.cqc.org.uk

11. The Law Society (2015) *Identifying a deprivation of liberty: a practical guide*, www.lawsociety.org.uk

12. Professor Sube Banerjee (2009) *The use of antipsychotic medication for people with dementia: Time for action, A report for the Minister of State for Care Services*, An independent report commissioned and funded by the Department of Health, www.rcpsych.ac.uk

13. NHS England (2015) *The use of medicines in people with learning disabilities*, 14 July 2015, Dear colleague letter, Publications gateway ref: 0389, www.england.nhs.uk/2015/07/14/urgent-pledge

14. M Crews, D Garry, C Phillips, A Wong, B Troke, A Ruck Keene, C Danbury, *Deprivation of Liberty in Intensive Care*, Journal of Intensive Care Society Volume 15, Number 4, October 2014

15. Department of Health (14 Januay 2015) *Update on the Mental Capacity Act and following the 19 March 2014 Supreme Court judgment*, Niall Fry, Policy Lead, Mental Capacity Act & Deprivation of Liberty Safeguards

16. Care Quality Commission (March 2015) *How CQC regulates NHS and independent acute hospitals, Provider handbook* www.cqc.org.uk

17. Local Government Ombudsman (2015) *Investigation into a complaint against Cambridgeshire County Council* (Reference number: 13 016 935) www.lgo.org.uk

18. Department of Health (2015) *The Seventh Year of the Independent Mental Capacity Advocacy (IMCA) Service 1st April 2013 – 31st March 2014* www.gov.uk/dh

19. Ministry of Justice (2015) *Family Court Statistics Quarterly January to March 2015 Ministry of Justice Statistics bulletin* www.justice.gov.uk

20. Department of Health (2015) *Mental Health Act 1983: Code of Practice* ISBN 9780113230068

21. House of Lords Mental Capacity Act 2005 Select Committee, *Oral and Written Evidence Volume 1 (A-K)* (2014) Q302

22. Local Government Association and the Association of Directors of Adult Social Services (2015) *Mental Capacity Act including the Deprivation of Liberty Safeguards An improvement tool,* July 2015, www.adass.org.uk

23. Care Quality Commission (2015) *How CQC regulates: Residential adult social care services Provider handbook,* March 2015, www.cqc.org.uk

24. Care Quality Commission (2015) *How CQC regulates: Residential adult social care services, Appendices to the provider handbook*, March 2015, www.cqc.org.uk

25. Courts and Tribunals Judiciary (2014) *Chief Coroner's Guidance No. 16, Deprivation of liberty safeguards (DoLS),* December 2014, www.judiciary.gov.uk

26. Piers McNeil, independent DoLS best interests assessor and trainer with Edge training and Consultancy Ltd

## Further Information

There are many sources of information on DoLS and the list below is not exhaustive but represents both official sources and the most reliable up-to-date commentary.

**Department of Health**
Niall Fry, MCA-DoLS Policy Lead, Area 313B, Richmond House, 79 Whitehall, London SW1A 2NS

E-mail: Niall.Fry@dh.gsi.gov.uk

**Social Care Institute of Excellence**
The government's main website on MCA and DoLS resources: *www.scie.org.uk/mca-directory*

**Mental Health Law Online**
Register for free regular updates on MCA and DoLS case law: *www.mentalhealthlaw.co.uk*

**39 Essex Chambers**
A leading barristers' chambers providing a monthly MCA and DoLS newsletter: *www.39essex.com*

**Mental Capacity Law and Policy**
A website written by a leading barrister in the field: *www.mentalcapacitylawandpolicy.org.uk*

**Edge training and consultancy** (both authors are directors)
Significant legal and policy updates on the MCA and DoLS plus training to health and social care professionals and DoLS assessors: *www.edgetraining.org.uk* email: *admin@edgetraining.org.uk*